OVER THE FARMYARD GATE

Country Life in the 1930s

A horseman leads his horse out of the yard, 1930. (Mr Hatley)

OVER THE FARMYARD GATE

Country Life in the 1930s

G.K. NELSON

ALAN SUTTON PUBLISHING LIMITED

For Irene

First published in the United Kingdom in 1995
Alan Sutton Publishing Ltd · Phoenix Mill · Far Thrupp
Stroud · Gloucestershire

British Library Cataloguing in Publication Data

A catalogue record for this book is available from the British
Library.

ISBN 0-7509-0866-1

Typeset in 11/13 Bembo.
Typesetting and origination by
Alan Sutton Publishing Limited.
Printed in Great Britain by
WBC Ltd, Bridgend.

CONTENTS

ACKNOWLEDGEMENTS

I am grateful to all those people who have helped in providing and collecting the material that has made it possible for me to complete the study on which this book is based. I am particularly indebted to those who have allowed me to publish either the written material, an edited version of their taped material, or the photographs they sent. I am also grateful to those whose information has helped so much in giving a background to the study which has resulted in the publication of this book and of three previous works. They will continue to provide inspiration for future work.

I am specially grateful to Sylvia and Ernest Kemp for their help with editing and typing this material, to Dennis Ward for help with the illustrations, and to my wife for proof-reading.

PREFACE

Since the Second World War life on the farm and farming methods have changed so rapidly that farming is a very different activity from that during the period between the two world wars. It was also a period of change but up to the Second World War the main sources of power were manpower and horsepower. It is true that these were being supplemented by steam and the internal combustion engine and also assisted by an increasing range of new machinery but it was not until the Second World War compelled us to rapidly increase our output of food that farmers turned to mechanization on a large scale.

Who would know more about life on the farm between the wars than farmers and farm workers? But these people seldom find time to turn their hands to literary work. Their reluctance to write has been a sad loss to the interested readers who have perhaps received a distorted view of farming and country life from writers whose knowledge is second-hand.

As a person who was brought up on a farm I have sought to extend the knowledge of farming life by collecting accounts of the experiences of over three hundred country folk. As a result this book contains a selection of first-hand accounts by farmers and farm workers. I have included cases from a wide range of agricultural environments in different parts of the country and the reaction of both farmers and farm worker to the changes that have taken place is recorded.

PREFACE

These stories take us into a world that has now vanished – a world that was very different from the one in which we live today. Not only was it a world in which most modern conveniences either did not exist or were too expensive for most people to possess but it was one in which values were very different. In those days family and friendship were more important than material possessions. On a material level, it was a world in which there was no electricity, gas or piped water in most rural areas, and in which the lavatory was a bucket in a shed at the bottom of the garden.

While many elderly people look back with affection on the 'Good old days', they also admit that life was hard and few would want to go back to the harsh living conditions of that time. However, they often point out that there was more friendliness and less crime than today, and that they could leave their houses unlocked with no fear of being robbed and walk the roads at night without being mugged.

This book stands on its own but it also complements three other books I have published namely, *To Be A Farmer's Boy* which is primarily concerned with the life of farm workers, *Countrywomen on the Land*, and my study of childhood entitled *Seen And Not Heard*.

Over the Farmyard Gate is illustrated with photographs taken by farmers and farm workers on the crude cameras available at that time, and these have been chosen in preference to professional photographs since they reveal much of the attitude of the photographer to his subject. I have also included some postcards since, although they had been taken by professionals, they were the most common form of communication used by ordinary people at that time.

CHAPTER ONE

FARMING IN THE EARLY TWENTIETH CENTURY

Farming in the first half of the twentieth century was influenced by two major factors: the state of the economy and the development of technology and farming methods generally. Let us first consider the socio-economic and associated political influences.

By the early years of the twentieth century England had almost completely recovered from the effects of the Great Depression of the 1880s and agriculture was becoming more prosperous. This prosperity was not being passed on to the farm labourers, however, and wages were about 12s (60p) a week in Norfolk, though a little higher in some other counties. Rises in the cost of living increased the discontent of the workers and led to strikes among the men. The St Faith's strike in Norfolk in 1910 attracted most attention. It dragged on for over a year but in the end the workers were defeated.

The victory of the Liberal Party in the 1906 election had been helped by the fact that farm workers had given their support to Liberal candidates in protest against the conservatism of farmers and country landowners. The conditions of the workers were improved by the passing of the Old Age Pensions Act in 1909 which alleviated some of the worries of elderly workers who dreaded having to retire to the workhouse when they could no longer do their jobs.

The agricultural depression of the 1870s and '80s had been largely caused by the free trade, *laissez-faire* policies of the governments of that period which permitted the unrestricted import of cheap food from abroad. This policy was, of course, popular with urban residents but was disastrous for the farming industry.

The British have a very ambivalent attitude towards farming. While there is a widespread sentimental attitude about the land and the countryside in general, it is only in times of desperate need that governments take any action to help the farming community or rural areas. This attitude has been demonstrated in the twentieth century and can be clearly seen when we compare government policies during the two World Wars with those of peacetime governments. The First World War led to an increased demand for home-grown food for two reasons: firstly, foreign exchange was needed to purchase weapons rather than to pay for imported food, and secondly, the increasing pressure of the German blockade made it more difficult to ensure the regular supply of food from overseas.

In consequence the government made every effort to increase the domestic production of essential foodstuffs. It effectively controlled the industry by introducing a system of subsidies and guaranteed prices for crops. As a result agriculture prospered and workers also benefited from a rapid increase in wages, which from 1917 were regulated by the Wages Board. Wages rose in the Eastern Counties from an average of 15*s* 3*d* (75p) a week in 1914 to a minimum of 37*s* 3*d* (£1.85) in 1919, and by 1920 the average for the country had risen to 46*s* (£2.30).

The situation changed rapidly after the war when a brief boom was followed by depression. In 1921 all government control of agriculture ceased and with it guaranteed prices and wage regulation. Prices and wages fell so that by 1924 the average national wage had fallen to 28*s* (£1.40). The depression had an equally bad effect on farmers and many went bankrupt. In some cases where farmers were unable to find a buyer for their land, farms were left derelict, sometimes for years.

2

The Great Strike of 1923 was caused by farmers attempting to cut wages and increase hours of work. The strike, which started in Norfolk, did little to improve wages but probably prevented wage cuts and increases in working hours. In the same year the Labour Government passed an act that established Wages Councils to replace the old Wages Board. These councils were set up in each county and empowered to set wage levels. This meant that the minimum wage differed from one county to another. In 1924 the councils raised wages by a few shillings: in Norfolk, for example, from 25s (£1.25) to 29s (£1.45) for a fifty hour week.

The agricultural depression continued throughout the 1930s though wages rose slightly – in Norfolk, to 34s 6d (£1.70) by 1938. Recovery did not come until the Second World War, when once more food production became essential to the war effort.

Let us now turn to the other causes of change in the first half of the twentieth century: the development of new technology and the introduction of new farming methods. At the start of the century there were two main sources of power on the farm, manpower and horsepower, although steam engines were being used on some. In 1910 there were 981,000 horses working on farms in England and Wales. When one considers that horses were also employed in transport in industry and for leisure activities, such as hunting and racing, there must have been at least two million horses in the country at that time. It is clear that the horse played a vital part in the economy of the country.

The prominence of the horse on the farm meant that the head horseman was the most important employee. He often acted as a sort of manager, particularly on large farms where the farmer needed such assistance. By 1940 the number of horses working on farms had been reduced to 541,000 and by 1965 to 19,000. This rapid decline was the result of the development of new sources of power and the increasing mechanization of farming. This also led to a decline in the number of workers needed. The decline in the number of people employed in the industry had serious effects on the social and economic life in the villages.

Change in farming methods is nothing new, it has been continuous from the time when crops were first cultivated as a more efficient means of providing food, and since breeding and keeping domestic animals replaced hunting as a means of providing meat. For thousands of years the primitive method of scratching the earth with a sharpened stick remained the only means of preparing the soil for the planting of seed. At first these 'digging-sticks' were pushed through the soil by human shoulders, but they began to evolve into ploughs that would be more effective and penetrate more deeply into the earth. At first these ploughs were pulled by human muscle power until it was realized that oxen could be used and in turn pull a heavier plough. Indeed the ox-drawn plough of our Anglo-Saxon ancestors remained in use on some farms until late in the nineteenth century. The introduction of lighter ploughs during the seventeenth and eighteenth centuries made it possible to use horses and with the coming of the Agricultural Revolution the ox was replaced by the horse as the main source of power on English farms.

During the Agricultural Revolution many implements were invented and new methods of farming introduced. Steam engines were in use on some farms by the middle of the nineteenth century. The first steam pump was used for land drainage in the Fens and was installed at Sutton St Edmund in 1818. The first steam engine used for cable ploughing was invented as early as 1634 by Heathcoat and Parkes. It was not, however, successful and a much improved system was introduced by John Fowler in 1856. This used a portable engine that had to be pulled by horses. Once in place in the field, it pulled a plough up and down by a rope attached to a system of pulleys. Within a few years Fowler had introduced steam traction engines that could move under their own power. Fowler steam ploughing sets continued to be used until well into the twentieth century.

The foot plough, from a postcard of about 1910. The foot plough was an early type of plough in which the depth of the furrow was controlled by a metal foot or skid in place of a wheel. (Author's collection)

The Norfolk plough was one of the most common ploughs used in the early twentieth century. It could be drawn by one or two horses. It was a single-furrow plough which was displaced by ploughs that could cut four or more furrows when tractors were introduced.

A Fowler steam engine being used to draw a cultivator across a field. An engine was placed on each side of the field and the implement being used here was attached to a hawser, which was wound onto a drum situated under the boiler of the engine. The two engines took turns to pull the implement backwards and forwards across the field. This photograph gives a clear view of the winding drum. The man riding on the cultivator had the job of steering. Such engines were also used to pull ploughs. (Mr B. Spreadbury)

Many attempts were made to use steam engines to pull ploughs and cultivators directly, but steam engines were too heavy to work successfully on the soft damp soil of Britain – they were more successful on the drier soils in America. Steam engines were used in a number of other ways on the farm, however, and most importantly to drive threshing tackle. They continued to be used for this purpose until they were made redundant by the introduction of the combine harvester.

Until the eighteenth century the main method of sowing corn was broadcasting by hand in which the sower walked up and down

Harrowing and sowing, from a postcard of about 1910. This illustrates the method of sowing seed by hand, known as broadcasting. The sower is preceded by a horse-drawn drag harrow, which opens up the soil to receive the seed, and by a chain harrow, which pulls soil over the seeds.

the field with a basket of corn hanging round his neck, throwing the corn rhythmically to left and right ensuring an even distribution of the seed. While seed drills are said to have been invented by the Chinese over four thousand years ago and used by the Romans, they seem to have fallen out of use and were unknown in England until they were reinvented in the seventeenth century. J. Sha in a book called *Briefe Discoveries of Divers Excellent Wayes and Means for Improving and Manuring the Land*, published in 1646, describes a machine which sowed seeds and distributed manure at the same time, but it is not known if this machine was ever brought into use. The first seed drill which is known to have worked was invented by Jethro Tull in 1700 and improved versions continued to appear throughout the eighteenth and nineteenth centuries.

Haymaking was carried out by hand until well into the nineteenth century, the hay was cut with a scythe, racked up by hand into haycocks, loaded onto carts, and taken into the barn, or built into stacks. During the nineteenth century horse-drawn reapers and rakes were introduced and more ambitious haymaking machines developed.

Corn harvesting was also done by hand well into the nineteenth century. The corn was also cut using scythes before being gathered into bundles known as sheaves and tied by hand. The sheaves were stood up leaning together in shocks (or stooks) to dry, and finally carted and built into stacks for storage until they could be threshed.

The first effective corn reaper was invented by Patrick Bell in 1828, but few seem to have been used until 1840 when improved machines developed by McCormick and Hussey in the USA were introduced into Britain. These machines reduced the amount of labour required to cut the corn, but the other tasks were still performed by hand. This was a foretaste of the mechanization that was to come and woud have devastating effects on the employment of farm workers and rural life.

The self-binder, which not only cut the corn but also tied it into sheaves, was first exhibited at Birmingham in 1874. These machines were not widely used until the early twentieth century. There are no reliable statistics for that period since the first statistics relating to reaper-binders were collected in 1942 when 101,907 such machines were in use in England and Wales.

Carting and stacking continued to be largely manual work but the introduction of the elevator reduced some of the hard labour of stack building. Thatching the completed stack was also a job that demanded highly skilled labour. The final process in harvesting, that of threshing the corn, had traditionally been performed by hand with the use of a flail which consisted of two sticks joined together by a leather thong. This method continued to be used on some farms until the beginning of the twentieth century, although by that time most of the threshing was done by machine. Early threshing machines were driven by horsepower but by the 1840s steam engines were being used and they continued for over a hundred years until the 1950s. Since threshing was an operation that only occupied a few days each year and threshing tackle was expensive farmers hired the equipment from contractors who also supplied the skilled labour necessary to operate the machines. The combine harvester, which carries out all the processes of cutting, drying and threshing the corn, was first introduced into Britain in 1928 from America where it had been found to be very effective in harvesting the vast plains of the Mid-West. They were only slowly adopted by British farmers because they were expensive and only economically viable on farms having a large acreage of corn crops.

One of the first combine harvesters seen in Wiltshire at Lower House Farm, East Everleigh, late 1930s. (Mr B. Spreadbury)

Indeed as late as 1939 there were only a hundred in use. Like the old threshing tackle, they were often owned by contractors who rented them out to farmers. By 1965 the number of binders in use had dropped to 41,650 while the number of combines had increased to 57,950.

The invention that replaced the horse as the main source of power on the farm was the internal combustion driven tractor. As we have seen steam engines had been introduced earlier but they had many limitations. Tractors began to be used in the early years of the twentieth century. The Sanderson Four Wheel tractor was introduced in 1906 and the first Fordson appeared in 1915. Many, however, were only prototypes and it was not until the inter-war period that they were more widely adopted. By 1939, however, 56,000 were in use on British farms. The Second World War provoked a rapid increase in their use and indeed government statistics show that by 1942 the number had almost doubled to 101,500 on farms in England and Wales. By 1966 the number had increased to 418,010.

During the inter-war period tractors developed in power and improved in quality and their introduction contributed to the development of other powered machinery. The gyrotiller, for example, was a motor-driven cultivator, first produced by Fowler in 1935. This made very deep ploughing possible, but since the machines were very expensive they were normally owned and operated by contractors. I can remember the excitement when a gyrotiller was used on a local farm!

The tractor also made it possible to use other heavy implements; for instance, while horses were still used to pull one or two furrow ploughs, a tractor could pull ploughs having six or more furrows, thus increasing the amount of land that could be ploughed in a day. The use of a tractor, therefore, reduced the number of horses and men required to undertake ploughing. This also applied to many other implements now used on the farm. Many of the processes such as cultivating, harrowing, drilling, planting, manure

An early light tractor of about 1920. (Mr Martin)

distributing, hoeing, potato picking, spraying, haymaking and harvesting could be speeded up through the use of new and heavier machines that were powered by a tractor. In some cases, as with the combine and the gyrotiller, the motor was incorporated into the machine itself, but in most cases the tractor was more economically efficient since it could be used to power a wide range of implements and machines. Its influence on the change in farming methods was prodigious.

11

CHAPTER TWO

FARMING IN SUFFOLK AND THE FENS

Mr H. Bye tells of his early childhood on a stud farm in Newmarket, Suffolk, and then goes on to describe farming in the Fens where many farmers had horse-drawn railways to carry their crops to the station, while others loaded produce on to barges which took it directly to local factories.

When I was six, my family moved to Plantation Farm, a racing stud farm near Newmarket in Suffolk. My father worked on the farm and looked after three Suffolk punches. Although Lord Derby's stable was at the farm, my father had nothing to do with the breeding of the racing mares and stallions, one of which was named Sansovina and won the Derby in 1924. The estate gamekeeper, Mr Davey, lived next door. We annoyed him sometimes when we took walks in the woods and disturbed the pheasants and other game birds.

In 1921 there was a drought so our well had to be deepened and we had to use a pump to obtain our water. During the work to deepen the well, a hoist was built over the top and a man called Sid Osborne released a wire and chain and the roller in order to lower Bill Challis to the bottom of the well so he could dig it out. Bill had to wear some leather waterproof long boots, as rubbers were not around in those days. It was his job to fill the bucket with chalk from the bottom of the well. Sid then wound it up to the surface, emptied it and returned it to Bill to fill again. This went on for two days. After a great heap of chalk had accumulated at the top of the well there was a mishap. The bucket reached the top but somehow fell back to the bottom before Sid could empty it. There was a mighty splash and Sid was relieved to hear Bill say, 'What the hell! I'm getting out, wind me up!' Bill came up in the bucket, vowing never to go down there again. Luckily, although there was a drought, the water did not run out again.

We used to go gleaning for corn for the chickens, a job we did not like. But we did like to see the horse-binders as my father worked one. In the hope of a cheap dinner scores of people with sticks would wait for rabbits to run out of the fields, away from the binders.

I remember when I was eight years old, my six-year-old brother and I came out of school one day and climbed over the red brick wall of Yew Wood to look for some twigs or plants for the next day's nature study lesson. The wood was privately owned and we stumbled across the gamekeeper with his two spaniel dogs. He was sitting in the shrubbery but when he saw us he jumped up and clouted my ear; we made a hasty retreat. He said he would tell my father and then give me another clout. But he didn't.

The parson in the village of Snailwell, near Newmarket, always had a full congregation on Sunday evenings. Two racehorse trainers would go round with the collection plate and the parson always had a chat with them before they left the church. When there was racing at Newmarket, the reverend gentleman was always at the racecourse. I was a member of the choir and received a half-penny for each service I attended. The landlord of the local pub was bass in the choir – he was a great friend of the parson. They would go rabbit shooting together and every springtime they painted inside the church. We could not get away from our school teachers. One played the twenty-pipe organ, which had to be hand pumped, while the headmistress also sung in the choir. If you sang a wrong note, you would hear about it at school on Monday. The parson was also a member of the fire brigade.

In 1926 when I was nine years old, we moved away from the racing world and went to live in a nine-roomed farmhouse in the Fens, 9 miles east of Ely. It took me a long time to settle. We went to the local school where we were taught by a schoolmaster and his wife, and an infant teacher. The schoolmaster was very strict and hardly a day went without someone being caned. I only had it once. There were 114 children in the school in one period around 1928. Money for Christmas was raised from whist drives and dances. I remember one Christmas at a dance, £12 8s 8d (£12.47½) was raised and each child was presented with a present, to the value of 2s 6d (15p), from Father Christmas. The Vicar would always put in an appearance before Father Christmas came, and then again just afterwards when he would say, 'What a pity I did so want to see Santa Claus. Now I must wait till next year.' The old 'Tortoise' coke furnace did not heat the school very well in the winter so the schoolmaster sometimes took us outside for drill to warm us up.

When I was fourteen I went to work on the farm where we lived. I was paid 13s (65p) for a fifty hour week. For extra money overtime was 3½d per hour. I very often worked with horses. Working with a threshing machine was a dirty job and the young lads mostly took the job of looking after the chaff with the rats and mice running around you as the stacks of sheaves were put on to the drum, as we called it. When you got to the bottom of the stack, there were always several dead rats.

Another job was working on a planting machine, a very boring job and a long day, but the overtime money was a great help. I paid 10s (50p) for my board at home but when I earned extra on overtime or piecework, the money was my own. It wasn't long before I had earned enough money to purchase a new Hercules cycle for £3 19s 9d (£3.99). I could cycle to Ely instead of paying the 11d (4½p) train fare or I could cycle the 26 miles to Cambridge instead of paying the 2s 9d (14p) return fare.

When I was 23 years old I married a 21-year-old girl. She had been a domestic servant for a shopkeeper, a publican, a parson and a doctor, so she was a good all-rounder when I married her. She became a part-time postwoman until we had a family. She rode a bicycle on her rounds but sometimes she had to get off and walk to the houses as the mud would clog up her cycle.

Most of the farmers would have horse railways so they could get their produce to the railway sidings, a mile or so away. They would then bring back to the farm seed potatoes, artificial manure and other supplies, delivered by the railway. There was a network of these railways from the farms to Shippea Hill station yard. The trucks were towed by trace-horses using skilled horsemen. Sir Frederick Hiam introduced these railways, having seen them in operation in Germany during the First World War. He also had some operating in the Littleport Fens.

Chivers, the jam manufacturers, owned their own locomotive for hauling their wagons – first steam, then diesel-electric, built by their own engineers. The station yard at Shippea Hill on one day had 136 rail wagons leaving. Queues of farm wagons would be waiting to go on to the weighbridge at the station yard. Every station yard was busy in those days. Shippea Hill had two freight trains leaving the station daily.

Much produce also travelled by road on steam wagons or old Thorneycroft lorries. As time went on the transport system was improved. Some sugar beet travelled to the factories by river. Horses and carts would negotiate the river banks where there was a chute which they called a jetty. Here the carts were tipped up and the beet would slide down into a barge. When fully laden with about 30 tons, a lighter would call daily and pick up the barges from the various points and take them to the Ely or Wissington factories.

On the land cauliflowers, cabbage and celery would be set by hand. The most celery plants I ever put in during a day was 2,900 in about ten hours, with help from a lady who dropped them ready for me to plant. Later the robot planting machine was introduced and was operated mostly by women. New potatoes were dug in the

Ploughing in the Fens on a cold winter morning, 1930s. (Mr Bye)

Seed drilling in the Fens, 1930. (Mr Bye)

A celery planter at work near Shippea Hill, 1930s. (Mr Bye)

Spraying celery in the Cambridgeshire Fens. 1935. (Mr Bye)

summer months with a fork with the help of a lady picking them up and putting them into sacks. It was very hard work.

Later in the season, when the skins of the potatoes were set, these would be lifted with a horse-drawn spinner and a hover which put them into rows. The women would then pick them up and put them into baskets. A horse cart followed the pickers and a woman or boy would catch the baskets of potatoes from the man who threw them in. When the horse and cart arrived at the end of the field, the potatoes would be tipped into long high heaps and strawed down. Later they were sorted with potato riddles, some by hand riddles and some by machine which were cranked by hand until petrol engines were introduced.

Sugar beet was drilled using men and horses. When the beet was big enough it was chopped out into bunches, and then singled out by a woman. Nowadays, the beet is planted by space drilling (that is, using a drill that can be adjusted to plant seed at set intervals). The sugar beet was pulled by hand when harvested and then laid out in rows. A cutting hook was used to cut off the top. As time went by a lifter, pulled by a horse, was used. A man then followed the machine and with a pick up chopping hook chopped off the tops and lay them in rows, before they were thrown into carts.

In the days of the horse railways, the beet would be loaded into tip-top trucks, taken to the railway sidings and transferred into rail wagons for the Ely beet factory. Sometimes in dry weather, the lorries would go direct to the field and pick up half a load before finishing loading at the roadside from the heaps. The horse railways were dismantled in about 1945/6.

One of the dirtiest jobs was threshing the corn from the stacks, which had been carted by horse and cart from the fields at harvest time. In later years this was done by tractor and trailer. Threshing sometimes took place in the harvest field, providing the land was solid enough to take the weight of the steam engine and drum. Some farmers, in the early days, used a portable steam engine hauling it from place to place by teams of horses, which was heavy going over the Fen droves. Since the Second World War these have been made into concrete roads which can take heavy lorries.

In 1931 I saw wheat sprayed in the springtime. The sprayer was pulled by horses. In due course farmers sprayed most of their crops, sometimes using aircraft to do the job. I have seen both fixed-wing craft and helicopters fly under electric cables. Sometimes pilots would come to grief – one collided with a Phantom jet of the RAF resulting in the death of three airmen. There have been many complaints about aerial spraying, and the practice is now restricted.

In the years between the 1920s and '40s, the farmers in the Fens irrigated their crops by draining the water-filled dykes to a higher capacity. If you were working with horses their hoofs would sink in but today water is pumped out of the main drains for overhead irrigation. Sometimes irrigation continues despite heavy rain.

Fen men called their morning break 'dockey'. Years ago, it consisted of a large hunk of bread with a hole cut out to place in the margarine or butter. Then they would have the meat, onion and cheese using their pocket knives to hack it off as required.

The threshing machine at work at Littleport, 1930s. (Mr Bye)

During the Second World War a cockney went to the Fens to be near his wife and child who had been evacuated from London. He worked for a farmer who sent him to clean up the barn on his first morning. At 10.30 a.m. some workers went past the barn on their bikes shouting out 'Dockey' but the Cockney fellow, not knowing what they were saying, carried on cleaning up. About half an hour later, they returned asking him if he had had his 'dockey'. 'Who is this darky fellow you keep on about?' he said. 'Your dockey, your lunch if you like. We call it dockey.' After it had been explained to him he made sure he was not late for dockey the next day. Nowadays workers carry sandwiches, very few old timers are left with their hunks of bread, cheese, onion and meat.

After the Second World War the concrete roads were built and lorries went to the farms to collect the produce, and rail traffic declined. Two trains started from Shippea Hill every day when the road traffic began to take over. When I was thirty-eight, I left the farm and took on a porter's job at the station dealing with yard work, being station signal lamp-man, and other duties which included working in the office after the clerk and station master had gone home, selling tickets, sorting out train enquiries, cleaning up and general station duties. Eventually, a vacancy came up for a signalman and I was appointed. I was a signalman for twenty-five years until I retired. Three years afterwards I left the countryside and went to live in the city of Ely.

Memories of Life on a Racing Stud, 1920

Every morning it is a lovely sight.
Race-horses passing with their colours so bright.
As we journey to our school each day,
We stand back and let them go their way.
Those stable lads have legs like match stalks.
They canter along our favourite walks.
There are several horses, quite a long string,

The lads are quite happy, some of them sing.
They were up early at break of the day,
Grooming, mucking out and bringing in hay.
Feeding the horses with their protein fare,
It must have been good as the manger's now bare.
They will be galloping on the heath for a while.
The trainer will watch as they complete the mile.
We live on a racing stud farm, where there are mares and foals,
Where there are lovely paddocks, not disturbed by moles.
Young fellow with barrow cleans up all the muck,
Wheels it away, it is filled to the buck.
The mares and foals take their daily graze,
Sun shines through clouds with its gleaming rays.
At 4 o'clock the stud hands come out,
Halters in hand, horses know what it's all about.
They shout 'Come On', horses run to the gate.
Halters on now, they are led away for their bait.
To the horse boxes they go, clean lovely and bright.
Horses then fed and bedded down for the night.
The male horse is stabled away from the mares,
He's taken out sometimes, where he goes to, nobody cares.
Sansovina is the name of that stallion horse.
The Derby he won on that Epsom Race Course.
In the evenings when the paddock is clear,
We run around and get out our sporting gear.
It is lovely living on a stud farm,
If you behave, you will come to no harm.
It's seventy odd years since I lived there,
I pay it a visit when I've time to spare.
Things have changed a lot over the years,
But the 'neigh' of a horse, one always hears.

H. Bye, Ely.

CHAPTER THREE

FARM WORK IN NORFOLK IN THE 1930S

Mr William Lambert, writing from Retford in Nottinghamshire, tells of his experiences of farming and country life in Norfolk. His accurately observed account of farming methods is well supplemented by details of the social life and everyday problems of farm workers.

I was born in the village of Hickling in Norfolk some seventy-one years ago in 1923 and lived there for the first nineteen years of my life. I left school at fourteen and went to work for Mr L.E. Borrett at Hall Farm until I left to join the RAF. The manual work was extremely hard and I was small in stature being 4 ft 10 in when I left school and only 8 in taller in 1935 when I left the farm. I found the work very testing.

In 1930 the hours for a day labourer spread over five and a half days were fifty-four per week for a wage of £1 10s (£1.50) with a deduction of 9d for health insurance. This deduction was for the worker only, it did not cover his wife or children if he was a married man. These wages remained fairly static for many years and I believe at the beginning of the Second World War they were only a few shillings more. Horse-keepers commenced work at about 4.30 a.m. to enable the animals to be ready for work at 6.30 a.m. which was the normal starting time in the summer and 7.00 a.m. in the winter – the winter hours largely depended on the daylight but overall during the year the hours averaged fifty-four weekly. Most farms had more than one horse-keeper so the pay varied. If a farmer stuck strictly to the rate fixed by the Agricultural Wages Board, the head horse-keeper, known in Norfolk as the team man, received £1 15s (£1.75) per week and the other horsemen £1 14s 6d (£1.72). Other farmers would pay all the horse-keepers £1 15s but sometimes with an extra 2s 6d (12½p) to the senior man. On a small farm where only one horse-keeper was employed he would normally be paid the fixed £1 15s.

Usually each horseman had about six horses to look after. On farms that had more than one horseman they would organize among themselves the feeding and grooming for Sundays. They did not have to start work so early then because Sunday was a day of rest and some could have a day off and a lie-in as they used to call it. Summer time was the best because after the day's work the horses would be turned out into a meadow for the night. In the winter they would be fed in the stable after work and the horseman would return at about 7 p.m. to bed them down with straw for the night, which was known as 'racking up'. Most farms had a pond and the horsemen would water the horses by letting them loose to have their fill before returning to the stable of their own accord. Where there was no pond a large trough was usually placed near the stable, very often with a pump attached to fill it. A number of horses would be led to the trough to drink at one time under supervision.

There were various feeds for horses, all of which would be made up on the premises. The usual was chopped oat straw or chopped hay mixed with rolled whole oats and bran. A very small portion of linseed or cotton seed cake would also be given once or twice a week, and long hay straight from the sack. Many horse-keepers had their own little secrets about caring for their charges and these were often handed down from father to son. Some would occasionally give whole mangold. Horses required a good diet and plenty of food for they worked very hard and needed to maintain their

Carting hay, 1930s. A wagon load is brought into the farmyard. (Mr Wilkinson)

strength. If a farmer was a poor feeder, it was evident from the condition of his horses. The horseman could always choose his team and work with the horses on the jobs for that day. Any day labourers who worked the horses had no choice and simply had those allocated to them. If there was work to do which did not require horses, this was always done by the day labourers.

The employment of cowmen, often known as yardmen, was similar. The pay was the same but the hours in the early morning were not required. On my farm there were about thirty cows and these were milked by hand twice a day. The cowman's day began at about 6.30 a.m. and milking was the first job. Mr Borrett assisted the cowman with this task because a milk delivery round had to be away by 7.45 a.m. at the latest. The cowman was responsible for the cleaning of the cowsheds, the dairy, for the feeding and bedding of the cows, and for any calves that might be on hand.

In the winter the cows were indoors or in the big yards for most of the time, but they were always turned out to a meadow for a period to give them some exercise. We had a pond from which the cows drank. They drank more than the horses, so large containers of about 10 gallons were placed in each feeding compartment in the cowhouse to enable them to drink during the night. The evening milking commenced at about 4 p.m. The milk was separated from the cream by a mechanical device-like cylinder which rotated at great speed by turning a handle at a steady pace. Anyone could do it but it took a little getting used to because unless the correct speed was attained the milk would not separate correctly. The cream was used for making butter and the whey was fed to the pigs. The morning's milk was always taken on the round after being put through a cooler and in those days that was the only treatment given. The quantity of milk in the morning was always greater than in the afternoon because of the longer time between the milkings. Several farms in the village used to sell milk but there

Storing hay in the barn – an alternative to stacking. (Mr Hatley)

25

was only one, other than ourselves, that delivered it. We had to collect it from the other farms. We had an arrangement with one farmer who sold all his milk wholesale to provide us with about 10 gallons a day which was collected on the round. The mik was delivered by pony and cart which was known as a float. There was a large churn holding 30 gallons which was held firmly on the float by a strong leather strap while milk in a smaller 2 gallon can was carried to the door. The milk was measured out with two ladles, one for half-pints and the other for pints. The milk was poured into any container, but usually a jug, supplied by the purchaser.

It was around about this time that the conditions for the supply of milk began to tighten up. All cows and handlers of milk had to be tested for tuberculosis and people dealing with milk for human consumption had to wear white coats. Health officers of the local councils would purchase milk at random and without warning. They always purchased a pint, half of which they handed back in a sealed container, the other half they kept for testing for tuberculosis, butter fat, cleanliness and added water. I am pleased to say we were always up to the required standard. I think 1933 saw the formation of the Milk Marketing Board which did not make much difference in its early days to farmers who retailed their milk, but it did to farmers who sold milk wholesale. In the summer months it was difficult to keep milk from going sour; most households used to scald (boil) it and stand the container in the coolest place they could find such as in a bucket of cold water. It was difficult on the delivery cart but we used to cover the churn with a white cloth to try and keep it as cool as possible.

We made butter from the cream of the surplus milk. It was always made on Tuesdays by Mrs Borrett, sometimes with a Mrs Watts, both of whom knew the tricks of the trade. The retail price of milk was 2½d per pint delivered and 2d a pint if collected. The butter was retailed at about 1s 3d or 1s 6d per pound. It was difficult in the summer when it was warm so we used to wrap the butter in cabbage or rhubarb leaves to keep it cool and reasonably firm.

The feeding of the cows was like that of the horses but with additional corn meal added to the feed to help the cows to produce as much milk as possible. Sugar beet pulp was also given.

In the winter cattle (bullocks) were purchased which were mostly Irish as there was a large trade in Irish store cattle in Norwich market. They were put into yards to fatten and sell for beef during the coming months. The cattle had to have attention seven days a week so a man was specially employed for this work and he was known as a bullock tender. On most farms this man would be employed as a day labourer during the summer months. His pay was £1 14s 6d (£1.71) per week and on our farm he looked after the pigs during the winter as well; in the summer they were looked after by the yardman. Some of the calves reared by ourselves would be put in with the cattle to fatten if they were not required elsewhere or sold as calves. There would be about 120–30 bullocks to feed and generally look after. They would be fed on hay, sugar beet tops (when available), sugar beet pulp, chopped straw, mangolds, turnips, linseed and sometimes cotton seed cake, barley meal and bran as well. Not all these things would be given at one and the same time but would be varied to give a palatable meal. The working hours of the bullock tender would not be fixed but he would start work between 6 a.m. and 6.30 a.m. working throughout the day until all his chores were finished for seven days each week during the winter months.

We kept 150 pigs for fattening in large strawed yards with open fronted sheds to shelter them from the weather. They were fed on dry meal from hoppers that would hold about 2 cwt each and given liberal supplies of water and whey to wash it down. They were also given green food such as kale or cabbage (specially grown for feeding pigs and cattle), mangolds and turnips.

On the farm we had a Ford tractor – a very different machine from those we see today. It was very difficult to start I remember; one started it on petrol with a starting handle and when it was nicely warmed up it was switched to paraffin oil. There were not many tractors about and I believe it was the only one in the village.

Most of the work was done by horse and manpower. The rotation of crops in our part of the country was much the same on all farms: a five year rota of wheat, mangolds, swede, turnips or sugar beet, and barley that was over-sown with seeds for hay which took two years to mature; some oats were also grown. The first crop was grass cuttings to make hay; these had taken two years to grow and were cut in the last week in May by a mechanical cutter pulled by two horses. These would usually work for about three hours when they would be changed for a fresh pair. If the crop was very heavy three horses would be used but this was not often necessary. The grass would be left for a few days and then it would be turned; this was done by a machine with revolving rakes drawn by two horses. Sometimes it would be turned again after another few days. The semi-dried grass was then put into large heaps called cocks. This was done manually by men with pitchforks. It was hard work and there was an art in making these cocks, so that should there be any rain it ran off and did not penetrate the centre and start the grass rotting. In some parts of the country these cocks were put on wooden platforms about 2 ft off the ground but this was not so in Norfolk. Several days later when it was thought the hay was ripe, the cocks would be pushed over to allow the sun and wind to penetrate for an hour or two. The hay was then carted to a convenient place and a stack made. The haystack was usually close to the buildings housing the cattle and horses so when it was required for fodder during the winter it was close to hand. The crop was loaded onto wagons or carts known as hermaphrodites and then pulled by two horses to the stack. A *morphor* (the local word for the hermaphrodite) was a tumbril with an extension added to the front to make it almost the same size as a wagon. A tumbril was a box-like cart, almost like a giant-sized wheelbarrow but on two wheels with shafts for one horse.

The work of stack making was an art because if the stack was not properly constructed the rain would penetrate it and the hay would be useless for fodder. Overheating was an additional hazard, and it was not unknown for stacks to catch fire because of this. The problem occurred if the material was not of the correct texture when it was stacked, so after the stack was completed iron rods would be inserted at various points to ascertain the heat. The construction of the stack would be done by the team man unless the farmer agreed with him to let someone else carry it out, which was most unlikely. There were no mechanical aids for this work and all the loading and unloading of the carts was done by men with pitchforks. Almost without exception farms employed boys – they were boys up until about eighteen years of age, then they were called a threequarter man until twenty-one, and at twenty-one they were men. Usually the driving of the horses and carts from the field to the stack was done by boys and this gave an early insight to how to control and work the animals. The fields would be left for a couple of months or so to enable another crop of grass to grow which would be cut again for hay, but of a much lower quality than the original crop. Otherwise cows would be allowed to graze it off and the permanent pastures left to recover and be used again at a later stage. After the stacks of hay had settled down and everyone was satisfied that all was in order, they would be thatched with wheat straw to help keep them dry. This thatching was done by one of the workers; not everyone was able to do it but most people who expected to remain working on farms all their lives learned how it should be done. There was no formal method of teaching, one just learned from another when the work was in progress.

After the hay harvest, known as *haysel* in our part of the world, there was something of a lull before the commencement of the corn harvest. During this period many odd jobs were done, such as cleaning out crew yards in readiness for the winter bullocks to come into, similarly cow yards, and horse and pig yards. Hedge trimming was also high on the list and cleaning up old straw stack bottoms and tidying up the place in general. Cow houses and dairies would be whitewashed and granaries and barns would be brushed out. On some farms hedge trimming was ongoing throughout the year, usually being done by retired employees to allow them to earn some extra money – the old age pension at this time was 10s (50p) per week and that was their only income.

The removal of the manure from the yards was also manual work; day labourers would fill the tumbrils and boys and horsemen would drive them to selected fields. Here the team-man would take over and tip the manure into a large heap in a corner to be distributed later. The tipping was done in an orderly manner, to produce a neat oblong stack about 8 ft high which would settle down after a few weeks to half its height. During this time the growing crops such as mangolds would also require attention to keep the weeds down. This was done by horse-hoeing using a tool bar with a number of blades attached and pulled by a horse. This implement sliced through the ground cutting off all weeds growing between the rows. The operation was usually carried out by two people, one leading the horse and the other steering. There was also a certain amount of hand-hoeing to be done to control the weeds growing between the plants and this would be done after the horse-hoeing. It was a really back-breaking job as one was continuously bending over. When the sugar beet, mangolds and turnips had grown to about 1½ in high they were far too thick and had to be singled out. This was done by a number of men, usually the day-labourers on piecework at so much per acre, using an ordinary hand hoe. The cutting blades were a different length for each crop: for sugar beet they were spaced at 6 in apart and for mangolds and turnips at 9 in. The men had to supply their own tools. The field had to be worked over twice in a period of three to four weeks so that there were single plants as far as possible. Each man worked the same row both times so the farmer, as well as the men in the gang, would know if someone was not doing his job correctly.

Depending on the weather the corn harvest commenced in late July or early August. The usual routine was dispensed with and the team man would discuss the situation with all the men and decide how many would be required. He would then discuss the matter with the employer and an agreement would be reached. There would be no standard weekly wages during the harvest time; it was a piecework job, known in Norfolk as 'taking work'. The going rate was £11 for a full man with subsequent agreed decreases according to age and ability for people under twenty-one years of age. Both sides agreed that if the harvest could be completed in under three weeks and three days everyone was happy – anything over this then no extra money had been earned. The whole idea was, of course, for the farmer to get his crop in with the minimum of delay and the men to be able to earn extra money for those with families relied on this to buy clothes. I well remember in some years the harvest lasted up to five weeks because of bad weather. It was usual in these cases for the farmer to give extra money but not all were so generous. I remember in 1934, I think it was, some corn deteriorated so much owing to wet weather that it could not be harvested and was given to the pigs as late as November.

During the harvest the horses had to be groomed and fed as usual, so horse-keepers were paid extra – about 5s 6d (26p) per week more than the normal weekly wage. Yardmen did not normally take part in the harvest but were allowed to earn extra by working overtime. This overtime was normally worked in the evenings and often it was connected in some way with the harvest. During this period no specified hours were worked and all concerned worked as long a day as possible, often until 10 p.m., but it was always dependent on the weather.

In those days wheat was the first crop to ripen because it was planted in the autumn and had a good start of some three or four months over spring-grown barley and oats. The situation is not the same today because in recent years a type of barley has been produced which can be planted in the autumn in the same manner as wheat, so it is now barley that is the first crop to ripen and to be cut. There was no oil seed rape in those days but one occasionally saw a field of linseed.

The corn field was first mown round the perimeter by men with scythes and the corn was bundled up and tied by hand as had been done for many, many years. This mown area enabled the reaper to go into the field. The reaper or self-binder was usually drawn by horses. It cut the corn off about 3 in above the ground, took it up into the machine, tied it into sheaves and cast them to one side. The binder was driven by one big wheel in the centre and the machine was held upright by another smaller wheel and a long pole affixed to the horses' collars. It was hard work for the horses pulling this heavy machine, so it was normal practice for a binder with a 5 ft cut to be drawn by three horses placed abreast of each other for periods of two hours before changing. It was best to have three sets of horses available for this duty. On our farm, where we had a tractor, this would be brought into use to pull the binder. The local blacksmith and carpenter modified the arrangement for pulling the machine to enable it to be done by both methods. Of course, the tractor was the best because it did not get tired but it did occupy two men, one driving and one on the binder, whereas when horses were used the man on the binder controlled the horses himself. Sometimes a boy would ride the middle horse if they were not very obedient. These horses knew their job; one would never work three young horses together, two would be old and the young one would learn from them. This practice was always carried out when more than one horse was required in any operation.

The sheaves of corn lying on the ground would be collected together, five rows being gathered into one bundle, which was then stood up on its end as a stook, known in Norfolk as a 'shock'. This was called shocking up. The shocks would remain in this position to allow both the straw and the ears of the corn to ripen. If these shocks were well prepared they would stand much resistance from the wind but if any were blown over, they had to be stood up as soon as possible. Not all the corn would be cut before carting commenced to carry in the corn to make stacks. It depended on the weather but the two operations would go on side by side for a time. It was more difficult on farms where there was no tractor but a plan was always worked out to obtain the maximum output.

Corn would be carried on the same sort of cart that was used for hay with the same method of driving to and from the stacks. Not all the corn would be stacked and sometimes some of it would be threshed out straight from the shocks. After the field had been cleared of the shocks, it would be raked with a horse rake, and the corn would then be heaped up and carted to the stack; then the places where the heaps had stood would be hand raked to ensure everything was collected. In the nineteenth century there would have been very little raking and the villagers would have been permitted to collect what was left in the fields for their own use. This was known as gleaning.

The stack was erected in the same way as the hay stack by the team man, except that they had sheaves rather than loose material. Much more thought, however, went into the construction of the stack. It could not be too big so the team man, sometimes with the

An early International tractor pulling a reaper-binder, 1920s.

farmer, would go to the field and estimate the amount of corn to be harvested and would then decide the size of the stacks. There were several considerations when deciding this: the stack had to store the correct amount for a reasonable day's threshing and it was essential that all the corn was stacked leaving nothing left over. When all the stacks were completed and all crops were in, the stacks had to be thatched as part of the harvest agreement; only then was harvest considered to be complete. The thatching of stacks should not be confused with the thatching of houses or barns for this was an entirely different job. Stacks were thatched with wheat straw while house thatching was mostly done with reed. This was a job for a professional who had to serve an apprenticeship of seven years.

In those days wheat straw was very long, some up to 6 ft in length. A load would be taken near to the stack and loosely shaken out in a heap, say, 36 ft long and 4 ft high. This would be doused with water and known as a bed. The straw would then be pulled

Carting corn, 1930s. A rack was often fitted to the front and back of a cart to increase its load-carrying capacity. A trace horse has been attached to help the horse in the shafts.
(Mr Wallis)

out by hand starting at the bottom of the bed with long straight lengths. These would be put onto stout sticks and fastened by string to form a big sheaf before being carried up a ladder to the roof of the stack where the thatcher would start at the bottom (the eaves) and overlap it to the ridge at the top fastening it down with long thin hazel sticks joined together with string. This was the same as that used on the binder to make the sheaves. When this was done correctly it would stand high winds.

It was the practice to have an altogether pay-off when the harvest was complete. This was a happy occasion as well as a serious one. Everybody was given a day off with pay but at about 11 a.m. everyone gathered in the kitchen of the farmhouse where beer, minerals, tea, sandwiches, pork pie and sausage rolls would be laid out to be devoured at will. The master would take each employee in turn into a separate room where one would receive any pay due after living expenses had been deducted. In the confines of this room with the boss and sometimes his wife too, one could express one's opinion about anything or anybody in complete confidence, and he would also tell you how you had performed. It all happened behind a closed door and rarely did any ill feeling occur.

At this meeting the men who had been engaged specially for the harvest knew they had finished their contract and would receive their final pay. They would also enquire about other contract work such as harvesting sugar beet when it was ready. This work was also done manually but sometimes the farmer was able to give it to his regular day-work labourers. But some of these men were also drift net fishermen and at the end of September were trying to get engaged on the herring fishing operating from Great Yarmouth and Lowestoft, for what was known as the home fishing, which lasted until Christmas.

It was also the place where the horsemen and the stockmen discussed their future. If any changes were to be made by either side it would be hammered out on this day and the effective date would be 11 October, Michaelmas Day.

The elevator made work easier for the stack builders. This elevator is being driven by a stationary engine. In the early days they would have been driven by horse power. (Mr Hatley)

The next day, unless it was a Sunday, was effectively the start of the new farming year. The next operation was the spreading of manure onto the hay fields. The day labourers would start loading manure into the carts (tumbrils) by hand, using four-tined manure forks, and the horsemen would unload them in the fields. It was usual to place the small heaps in rows 20 ft apart and the heaps 20 ft apart. There would be seven heaps to the load. This manure would then be spread over the field by men using forks. Once this had been completed ploughing would commence, deep ploughing 10 in to 1 ft deep to bury all the grass and the manure. This was carried out by horse plough with two horses to a single furrow plough. A man would plough 1 acre per day and would walk 10 or 11 miles. On our farm we would use the tractor if possible, which would pull a specially built plough of two furrows. The tractor would only be able to travel at about the same speed as the horses but would complete twice as much work. The horses would cease work at

11.30 a.m. when they were brought home, watered and given a good feed and rested until 1 p.m. Then they would go back to work until the normal finishing time of 4.30 or 5 p.m. After a few days the newly turned soil would be rolled and harrowed to produce a seed bed into which the wheat would be drilled. The roll was drawn by two horses; harrows are like large rakes also drawn by two horses. The seed drill was rather a heavy affair; it consisted of a long box into which the corn was tipped with tubes protruding from the bottom which guided the seed into the earth. At the end of the tube was a solid disc which cut into the ground and the seed fell into the opening it made. The amount of seed released from the box into the tubes could be adjusted to meet the need. The number of horses required to pull the drill depended upon its size: a 6 ft drill would require two horses, a 10 ft width would require three horses. The operator would walk behind the drill and guide the horses with reins and he could see that no blockages occurred in the flow of the seed. A tractor could be used but it required two men, one on the tractor and one behind the drill. It would work at a faster rate than the horses so a platform had to be built onto the drill for the man to stand on and move about in case the tubes became blocked. After the drilling the field would be harrowed again with a lighter type to ensure all the seed was covered and the land would then be left for the seed to grow.

At the same time as the planting of wheat was proceeding other men would be ploughing the stubble of the barley (unless it had been over-sown the previous year for hay) and oat fields to a depth of about 3 in. The stubble would then be harrowed or cultivated out. A cultivator is an implement with large thick tines fixed to a heavy toolbar and could be adjusted to go deep into the ground. This implement was not used very much but it did a good job if there had been any quantity of large weeds in the previous crop. The disturbance of the stubble would enable it to be burned in small heaps known as 'quicks' over the field. If the weather did not allow this, it would be carted off into one heap in a corner of the field, and allowed to rot; after two or three years it would be carted back and spread over the field. This shallow ploughing was known as 'skimming'. These fields would then be left until spring.

During the late summer, store cattle would have been purchased and put onto the marshes to graze. At the end of September or early October, they would be brought into the yards to be fattened over the winter months and the bullock men would leave their day-work friends to attend to them.

The next operation would be the sugar-beet harvest. This was manual work and back-breaking. It was piece work for the men who lifted the crop but not for the men who carted it off the fields. On some farms the beet would be ploughed out, which could be done with an ordinary plough. However, this was not very satisfactory, so a special plough with two plats (the part that turns the soil over) would be used. It had to be set very deep into the ground as sugar-beet roots are like parsnips and go down a long way. It would be pulled by two horses and the beet would be loosened and lifted a few inches. The other method was for a man to use a small spade-like tool which was 1 ft long, 3 in wide at the bottom and 6 in wide at the top attached to a short handle, giving an overall length of some 2½ ft. The tool would be plunged down alongside the beet to lever it up and out. In each case, after lifting the beet would be knocked together to remove as much soil as possible and laid in neat rows with the tops all facing the same way. The next operation was to remove the tops by cutting them off with a sharp hook (a sickle) with about 2 in of the beet itself so that all traces of green were removed. The beet would then be thrown into heaps some 9–12 ft apart, the tops being left where they were. I have seen the tops cut off with a spade while lying on the ground but this method was not very satisfactory and the topped beet had to be loaded into the carts by hand instead of with a fork. At this point the pieceworker had completed his contract. The rest of the work was mostly done by the regular day-work labourers; extra men would only be brought in if there was a large acreage.

The prepared beet would then be loaded onto carts (tumbrils) and taken to the roadside or just inside the gate of the field and left in large heaps. The carts used for this would be tipped up when possible. They were constructed to enable this to be done without removing the horse from the shafts. As the heaps got higher and larger one would off-load by using a fork. This was a special tool larger than an ordinary four-tined fork, shaped and having ten or twelve tines each with a small knob on the end so as not to prick the beet. The beet would then be picked up by contractors' lorries, being loaded by manual labour using a fork. Sometimes they would be conveyed to the nearest railway station and loaded into trucks but as lorries became bigger they would be taken direct to the factory. If the weather was dry, however, one could use just one horse to remove the beet from the field, but if it was wet and muddy it would take two horses to pull the cart which made the job much slower.

The first sugar-beet factory was built in 1912 at Cantley in Norfolk and was a Dutch venture. Sugar beet had been grown in Holland for some time and the Dutchmen thought it would do well on the soil of East Anglia. Initially the factory was operated by the Dutch but in 1914, at the outbreak of the First World War, they were interned and the British Government took over the running of the factory, which has been run by the British ever since.

Each farmer who grew this crop under contract was obliged by the terms of that contract to take back an amount of the pulp. This was governed by the tonnage of the beet he had sent into the factory. The farmer also had to take back the soil which accumulated when the beet had been washed. I think there was also some agreement about lime but I am not sure of the details of this. Some farmers, however, were supplied with lime to spread on the fields. These practices are not operative today and the by-products of beet are marketed just like any other commodity.

After harvesting the beet it was usual to cart off the tops and feed them to the bullocks now established in the crew yards. The tops would be taken to the shed near the cattle but the feeding would be done by the bullock tender. Some would be given to cows but the amounts would be carefully monitored because over-feeding would taint their milk. The beet would be spread over a wide area on the meadows so the cows had plenty of space to consume them. Some farmers who kept sheep would graze them where beet was grown. Occasionally the tops would be ploughed in as manure.

Towards the end of September the nights got cooler and the horses and cows were brought inside during the night. While the roots harvest was in progress, some men would be carting straw for bedding to keep the animals warm, and dry hay would also be brought in for them to feed on. The method of getting hay from the stack is interesting. The stack would be cut into small sections as required using a large knife, so that only a small amount of the stack was exposed at one time. This kept the chances of it getting wet to a minimum. Straw was different; one started at the top of the stack and removed it as it came. The chances of it getting wet were minimal as new straw was being taken away almost daily.

After the sugar-beet harvest came the harvesting of mangolds and turnips. When this work was started the weather would be much colder and wet in late October to early November. Mangolds would not stand frost so these were gathered first. A man would go along the rows and trim off most of the green top as they stood in the ground. He would be followed by men with horses and tumbrils who would pull the tops up by hand and throw them into the carts. These would then be taken, put into long heaps some 15 ft wide and made like a pyramid, near the field gate. These heaps had various names such as clamps, banks, hales and pies and would be covered with straw or bracken followed by earth dug from around the base to about 1 ft thick, except for a small vent left at the top to let out the heat. The same operation would be carried out for the turnips but only a little earth would be put on top of the straw because they can stand some frost. Sometimes the turnips would be left in the ground as long as possible and taken direct to the cattle shed or the meadow for the cows once all the sugar-beet tops had been cleared.

At this time of year not much would be happening on the arable land; a little ploughing might be carried out if it was possible up to about Christmas. About a fortnight before Christmas the turnips and mangolds would have to be carted from the clamps to feed the cattle and although the cows would be turned out for an hour or two each day, there would be no grass for them to graze. The number of day labourers at this time was down to a minimum.

As soon as possible after the beginning of the new year, tilling of the land for the spring crops would begin depending on the weather and a real start would be made about mid-February. The fields that were to become hay would be chain harrowed. A chain harrow is something like chain link fencing only very much heavier and flexible. It would be pulled by two horses and would break all the molehills and other lumps. The ground would then be rolled with a heavy roll; this was to firm the soil around the roots of the grass. Nothing more would be done to this crop until it was harvested.

Ploughing, harrowing and rolling to get a fine seed bed would now proceed for the spring sowing of barley and oats. These would be planted in the same way as the wheat and every effort would be made to have it in by the end of March. If a field was to be manured, this would be done in the same way as for wheat but it was always done before ploughing so that it could be buried. Not all fields would be done at this time because sufficient amounts of manure had been put on over the four or five year cycle.

The same effort went into the preparation of the land for the crops of sugar beet, mangolds and turnips. No manure, however, was put on as it effected the growth and the shape of the roots. But the preparation was even more concentrated for these root crops because the tilth had to be finer. The method of planting was different from corn. The field would first be ridged and the drill covered two ridges at a time and was drawn by one horse; usually an old, steady animal was used. The operation could be controlled by one man guiding the horse with reins but if this was not possible, one man would have to lead the horse. Sugar beet and

41

mangold seed is large, about ⅛ in across and very rough on the outside. The inside of the drill box where the seed was put had small cups which revolved when the machine was in motion and tipped the seed down a pipe which led to the ground to a drill made by a disc. A small roller then covered it up. Turnip seed was altogether different, very small, about the size of a pin's head, and the machine had to be adjusted so that only the minimum amount required was put in. This work would be done during April and the field would not be touched for some weeks until the seed was well up.

After the new year, the bullocks which were fat enough for slaughter would be sold off, a few each week, either at the market (in Norfolk we always referred to them as a sales) or to a butcher. This would gradually reduce the work of the bullock man and he would be available for other work with the day-work labourers until all the bullocks had been disposed of, usually by the middle of April. He would then be a day-work labourer until the next autumn.

The first week of December onwards saw the stacks of corn being threshed at regular intervals. The times this operation took place depended mainly on one of three things: whether the farmer required straw because his stocks were getting low, the price of corn on the Corn Exchange, or whether he needed money to keep going. If he required straw the corn threshed out would be stored in sacks in the barn to wait for a favourable price. If the price at the Corn Exchange was right, arrangements would be made with a merchant to collect it although it may have had to be stored for him for a short while. If the problem was a shortage of working capital the merchant would come and collect it direct from the threshing machine to enable the farmer to have his money.

When the barley, wheat and oats had grown to a height of about 2 in, they would be harrowed with light harrows to disturb the soil and assist in destroying small weeds. Rolling would follow to firm the crop around the roots. The crop would then be left until harvest except for weeding. This was done using a tool called a dock spade or spudder (a long straight blade about 3 in long by 2 in wide on a long handle) to destroy docks and thistles. By the end of May all this work would end to enable the hay harvest to start again.

I think the biggest change by far in farming life during the past fifty or so years is the huge decline in the number of people employed. On the farm on which I worked and have largely based my story, there are now only two men and the farm is considerably larger. Other changes concern the buying up of small farms by city organizations which make them into large units specializing in only one or two crops. The vast amounts of expensive machinery now used are owned by these large units. The growth of contractors who now do the work for the small farmer enables the ownership of machines to be kept to a minimum. It does not make sense for the small farmer to try to own machinery such as combine harvesters, sugar-beet and potato-lifting machines which are only used for a few weeks each year.

The use of silage for cattle seems to have altered altogether the feeding habits of bygone years. The vast use of pesticides and similar concoctions which were never heard of before have also changed farming. The huge advances in seed supplies have also altered agriculture. In my day all corn was dressed on the floor of the barn with blue vitriol – a powder dissolved in water and thrown over the pile of seed which was turned over by hand two or three times to wet it all. This dressing kept pests like weevils and wire worms that live in the soil at bay, but it was not very good for the birds. This practice has been illegal for some years and all seed is supplied by merchants duly treated to government specification. Sugar beet and similar seeds are now supplied coated with a mixture unknown to me, which enables them to be space drilled so that singling with the hoe is unnecessary. Today the quantity of seed required is less and is known as rubbed seed.

No artificial manure (tillage) as supplied now was used; very occasionally basic slag and guano was used. Lime was spread at intervals as was soot. Chimney sweeps in both town and country would store the soot for about one year before selling it to the farmer. The soot had to be old as new soot would kill the seed.

It is many years since I have seen or heard of a mole catcher. All farms had this service, usually provided by a man who killed all kinds of vermin such as rats, mice and rabbits. Payment was made at a few pence per mole and the catcher kept the dead animal which he would skin. Then he would stretch it out on a board to dry and after treating with saltpetre, it would be sold to the fur trade. Rats and rabbits would be hunted with ferrets and the bolting animals would be shot, providing the farmer and his friends with a day's sport. Payment for this would be on a daily basis. The rats would be disposed of by burying them and the rabbits remained the property of the farmer, who would sell them to a butcher or a game dealer. Mice would be poisoned.

The varieties of corn have greatly increased and plant breeding has made big strides. Many strains have been bred and the stems are shorter so there is less to dispose of. The yield of corn per acre has increased: a ton of wheat or barley was considered to be a fair return, now 3 tons per acre is a normal output.

The tied cottage was much in evidence fifty and more years ago. Most farmers had them and farmers also hired from other landlords. The cottages caused much heartbreak when the employee either had a difference of opinion with his master and had to move out having no other position to go to, or became old or ill and no longer fit for work. It was very easy to have a tenant evicted; a court order was easily obtained and the tenant had no safeguard as they have today to be re-housed as a homeless person. I saw several of these happening and they were a sorry sight, especially when children were involved or it was a wet day. Sometimes a family could find temporary accommodation but it was usually unfit to live in. Some families were in favour of the tied cottage arrangements because no rent had to be paid, whereas if one was lucky enough to obtain council accommodation, one had to pay rent which was not recoverable from the employer. I well remember in 1929 some council houses had been built in our village; my parents moved into one (my father was not a farm worker) at a rent of 3s (15p) per week, but for a farm worker it was 1s 6d (7½p) per week, but when the weekly wage was only £1 10s (£1.50) per week, every shilling counted.

Some farmers insisted the employee lived in a tied cottage as he then had a better hold over them for the services he required. If by chance, a family with children had not found accommodation by nightfall the authorities would step in to safeguard the children who would be removed to the workhouse with the mother. The Poor Law Act was in operation at that time. The father could also seek refuge in the workhouse but would be separated from the rest of his family. No provision was made for the furniture which would remain on the roadside so the father would usually remain with the furniture. I don't think I saw anyone in these circumstances for more than a few days before something turned up, albeit sometimes very primitive.

The position with the sick and elderly who suffered this fate was usually a disaster for them. The retirement age was seventy so in many cases these old people, who had given their lives in service, either went to live with relatives or went to the workhouse. Some were very happy living with their families, for others it was a struggle to fit in but it was worse going to the union (workhouse) where couples were separated. In recent years some farmers and landowners have made provision for their retired employees by making accommodation available but this is the exception rather than the rule and today more old people's bungalows are available. There are also fewer tied cottages today with the changes in the employment of manpower.

A sport that is no longer possible is the chasing of hares and rabbits in the harvest field. I said sport because that is what it seemed to all concerned at the time. When fields of corn were being cut with a self-binder, it was usual for the field to be finished during the evening. The standing corn was home for hares and rabbits and it was natural for them to congregate in the centre. As the area of standing corn was reduced, they would eventually make a break to try and get to a safe haven such as the hedgerow surrounding the field. During the evening many people would gather in the field, boys, girls, teenagers and grown-ups as well, all armed with sticks. When the hares and rabbits made the break all would chase them from every direction and if possible kill them with the sticks they carried. Some got away but most never had a chance. Some landowners forbade this practice and had the sport for themselves by shooting the animals. It was very dangerous to have runners and guns together so they rarely mixed. Anything killed was by tradition the property of the workers, so at the end of the day the workers were given the opportunity to have a pick of the catch, the remainder would be auctioned off there and then and any money was put into a fund which was used by the men to purchase beer for the harvest period.

The permanent grass meadows were always a source of trouble in some way, mostly because of weeds. When one kept cattle there must always be an amount of permanent pasture and as near to home as possible. It takes several years to produce good pasture so it was a treasured field. The scourge of these fields were weeds such as buttercups which cattle and horses did not like because of their bitter taste, ragwort which is poisonous to all animals, and thistles, nettles and docks. There were no sprays to counteract these weeds, they would simply be cut down. But after a time the weeds would have the upper hand and the only remedy was to plough the field and start again. It was usual to plant with wheat the first year after ploughing up, followed by a crop of roots, mangolds or turnips, which through all the hoeing that went on cleared most of the weeds. This was followed by barley which would be over-sown with hay seeds mixed with permanent grass seeds. The hay would be cut in the usual manner but instead of ploughing up again it would be left as a meadow and used as such until weeds became a problem again.

In East Norfolk, we were surrounded by marshes and these were extensively used for grazing. In the main they could only be used during the summer months because in the winter they would flood; they were also very exposed and unless some form of shed or shelter was erected, not many animals would stand the winter here. In addition to feeding stock on them, many grew rushes which would be cut and dried and used for bedding cattle together with straw. On a few of the marshes, a form of grass used to grow up to some 2 ft high, which was mown and used for fodder and known as marsh hay. It was a low quality product and not widely used. The cutting of these marshes was essential to enable a crop of rushes for the following year. If left, the rushes just died down and eventually the marsh would be of no use for grazing. During the Second World War, the marshes were taken over by the Government and managed by the local War Agricultural Committee. They were drained and crops of corn and potatoes were grown, making a large contribution to the food shortage. After the war they were returned to their original owners, some continued to be cultivated but the majority returned to grazing land.

With the advent of the combine harvester, no stacking of corn is necessary. Corn is threshed as it is cut but it has not been dried out so it has to be artificially dried. Barns have been modified to enable the corn to be tipped and hot air is forced through the heap to dry it. It is rather an expensive operation so the drier the corn can be cut, the better. The air is heated by electricity, oil or propane gas and forced through ducts into the corn by a large fan running at great speed. If a farmer is not in a position to have this equipment, arrangements are made with merchants who have large stores and who buy the grain direct from the harvester and dry it themselves.

Today there are farm co-operatives and they are many and varied. A farmer will own and farm his land as he pleases but may join forces with a number of others to form a co-op for, say, potatoes when they agree on the number of acres to grow and to sell them through the one channel. They also exchange manpower and machinery for the cultivation and harvesting of the one crop, saving money as not all of them will own machines. This is also done for corn, sugar beet and peas. Nothing of this kind was in operation fifty years ago.

CHAPTER FOUR

LIFE AS A FARM PUPIL IN SURREY

Mr A.J. Lessware of Bishopsteignton, Devon, sent me a diary he had kept when he was a farm pupil in 1933. This gives a very good account of the jobs that had to be done throughout the year and I have used it to supplement the other information he sent.

I got into farming quite accidentally. My elder brother went to Wye College in Kent and after obtaining a BSc degree in Agriculture went to work in Ceylon in 1929. When I left school in 1930 he suggested that I should work on a farm for a year and then he would take me back to Ceylon with him and put me on an estate to train as a manager. However the slump came, he was paid off and I was left to fend for myself.

The first farm I went to as a pupil while living at home was at Ottershaw in Surrey. It was of 120 acres, 60 of which were arable. There were two carters (horsemen), a cowman and two general farm workers. The oldest man had been champion ploughman, champion rick builder and champion thatcher of the district. We used to have our midday meal in the harness room of the stables and then old Henry would have a 'nap' and woe betide anybody who made a noise and woke him up before it was time to start again.

LIFE AS A FARM PUPIL IN SURREY

From the diary we learn that during January and February 1933 he spent much time muck spreading, hedging and repairing chicken houses. One day Blossom, the horse, had the gripes and he had to walk her round the yard for two hours. For a week he stood in for the cowman who was sick.

In March he was still muck carting but spent most time ploughing and harrowing. In April he was cultivating, harrowing, rolling and drilling mangold seed. During May he was couching (removing couch grass), harrowing and drilling.

In June he was cutting, raking and stacking clover. He was also hoeing mangolds and mowing hay. In July it was haymaking, harrowing turnip fields and drilling turnip seed. In August, it was stooking corn but there was little corn grown since this was mainly a dairy farm. He was also cutting clover and hay, thistles, and ferns (probably bracken which was used for litter in cowsheds and stables).

By September he was carting kale, dung carting and hedging. In October, ploughs were repaired before ploughing, and mangolds were pulled.

During November it was mangold harvesting, and spreading basic slag. Slag is a by-product of steel production. It is rich in phosphate and lime and is used as a fertilizer.

In December there was more slagging, dung carting and also milking. He worked over Christmas.

The work at Ottershaw was all done with horses and the cows were milked by hand. The hay was cut by a horse-drawn mower and the corn by a binder. The hay and corn were put into ricks. When the hay was wanted in the winter it was cut out with a hay knife and carted to the cowsheds or the stables to be fed to the cows or horses.

The corn ricks were mainly built on platforms supported by staddle-stones so that the rats could not get at them. The hay ricks were built so that the middle was always higher than the outsides; that way the rain always tended to run off. The sides also overhung the top so that after thatching the eaves dropped the rain clear of the sides. The same applied to the corn ricks, but it was more meticulously done. The sheaves were laid round the outside first on each layer with the ears inwards and the knot of the string upwards. The next layer was laid with the butts of the sheaves just overlapping the string of the last row and so on into the middle, so that the middle was always higher than the outside.

The mangolds were grown in rows and then when big enough were singled out to 9 or 10 in apart. Later we hoed between the rows. In the autumn they were pulled and the leaves twisted off. When the weather was frosty they were left in heaps and covered with leaves to keep the frost off until they could be carted to one big clamp where they were first covered with straw and then with soil. Mangolds cannot be used for feed until after Christmas as they are not ripe. Swedes were used up to Christmas and were pulled and fed straight from the field.

It was a very good, well-run farm for the 1930s, compared with many farms in the Eastern counties which were derelict. It was run on the four-course rotation method of roots, barley or oats followed by clover ley, and then wheat. The roots would be grown on land that had been in wheat the year before. The ground would be dunged and ploughed, then cultivated to get rid of any couch grass. Hoeing killed more weeds. The next year barley or oats were grown. They were drilled in the spring after the roots had been carted off and the land ploughed and worked down. After the barley was up about 6 in high the one year ley of broad-leaved clover and Italian rye grass was sown using a 'Shendy Box' which consisted of a long box mounted on a wheeled frame; it was very light and was pushed by one man. The seed was pushed out by brushes driven by the wheels. The one year ley would come on after the barley was harvested and the following year would be cut twice for hay. The hay was preferred for horses.

In the autumn after the second cut of hay the clover was ploughed in and would provide humus and nitrogen from the nodules in its roots. It was a system which kept the land in good heart, grew good crops and did not produce a mountain of expensive unwanted surplus!

After I left Ottershaw I got a job on a gentleman's farm in Sussex. I was sent out the first morning (after having helped to milk a dozen Guernsey cows who managed to give 10 gallons) to harrow some grass fields. It was a beautiful spot looking away to Beechy Head but the horses were weak and covered with lice, the harness was tied with string and I had come from a well-run farm where the horses went out with all their brasses shining, so I gave a week's notice and cycled home 85 miles. I then went to another farm in Surrey where I lived in but that wasn't much better. So after six months I moved again and went to Pound Farm near Ripley in Surrey where I lived in. I stayed there until we moved down to a farm near Fareham in 1934.

At Pound Farm I started work by 5 a.m. and first fed my horses before going into the cowshed to help milk the cows. After that I went back to the stable to brush down the horses and harness up. When that was done I went in to breakfast at about 8 a.m. and was out again by 8.30. I was working with the horses all day. It was a good farm to get experience. I finished at five in the evening, but in the summer it could be 10 p.m. before I finished because I did all the horse work (ploughing, carting and so on).

Looking back when I ploughed with horses I didn't 'Homeward plod my weary way'. I went home very pleased with myself if I had had a good day's ploughing, and especially if some elderly countryman had come past and said, 'Not bad Boy'.

Living in then was a very quiet life. Mr H had an armchair one side of the fire in the winter and Mrs had the other armchair. I sat at the table in a straight-back chair, and having bought myself a set of Dickens' novels (sixteen volumes) got through them in about twelve months.

I cycled to the cinema once or twice a week, about 7 miles away. I left my bike with lamp, pump, cape and leggings in the saddle bag at the back of the cinema and never lost a thing. I don't think you could do that now!

Going home, 1930s. Like Mr Lessware, another cheerful horseman leads his animal home after a good day's work. (Mr Poole)

could do that now!

My pride and joy at Pound Farm was a magnificent wagon which could be used with either single shafts or double shafts. When I went to the station to collect loads of feed I used the double shafts and drove the two shires in them. I used to back the wagon into the loading bay at the station. Normally I used a trace horse in front.

The farm was a mile off the Portsmouth road behind the Witley Pools. I believe the M25 is near or over it now. In the Eastern counties where I had worked before wagons were called wains. The hay wain in Constable's painting is not a wain but a limber wagon

Fill horse and trace horse. When pulling a heavy load two horses were used. The fill horse between the shafts was helped by a horse in front, which was attached to the cart with chains known as traces.

for the pole can be quite clearly seen.

The term 'wain' seems to have been used for any type of wagon including those with poles as well as those with shafts. J.M. Wigeon in The Rural Cyclopedia *(1847) defines a wagon as, 'A large four-wheeled carriage, for the conveyance of heavy loads', and he went on to say, 'wagons are very various in size and structure, according to the different uses which they are intended to serve; and even agricultural wagons are exceedingly diversified, according to the mere custom of counties or to the taste of caprice of individuals'. Wigeon's description remained valid at least up to the middle of the twentieth century.*

In the autumn of 1934 just before my twenty-first birthday, I went to Avoncroft College which was then at Offenham near Evesham but which moved to Bromsgrove the following year. I

Tony Lessware driving a tractor, photographed by Cecily Lessware (then Bounds) with a Brownie box camera, June 1939.

cannot speak too highly of Avoncroft and all the staff who ran it. I met a lot of young men of my own age to discuss things with. We also met a lot of people in agriculture including Professor John Hammond of Cambridge and Professor Wilson. George Cadbury would come and talk in our Common Room and even come out to the kitchen where we had a rota for washing up.

After I left Avoncroft I went to Hampshire for a year and then to Moulton Institute of Agriculture in Northampton for another year.

Farming changed mainly during the Second World War and soon afterwards. The two biggest changes were the introduction of the milking machine and the tractor.

Machine milking was not universally accepted for a long time because nobody knew anything about it. When man first started milking cows he used a warm hand and did what a calf does when it sucks. When the milking machines were first used they were put on after the cows had been washed with cold water. It was thought a bit sissy to use warm water. In large herds somebody would wash them well ahead of the machine and by the time the machine was put on the milk had gone. I should explain that when the calf starts to suck or the cow is washed, preferably with warm water, a message goes from the udder to the brain which sends back an instruction to the mammary gland to pump a substance into the blood surrounding the vessel containing the milk in the udder. The muscles surrounding the vessel contract and force out the milk down the teat. The milk will come in about ten seconds if the cows are washed in warm water. But unless the machine is put on straight away the milk will stop coming. I found out later that the warm water was not the main cause of the let-down reflex but the massaging of the udder when washing. The udder can be sprayed with warm water to wash off the mud which will not have any effect. The milk can then be made to come by washing the udder in the ordinary way when the machine is ready to be put on.

Another big change over the years is the disappearance of the hedges and in some places the banks. They were planted for a reason, apart from dividing the farm into fields. The horizontal banks on steep fields were there to stop erosion of the soil after the fields were cultivated.

There have been considerable changes in animal health. My father was taken on by the Veterinary Department of the Ministry of Agriculture in 1890. The only qualifications he had were in butchery and the ability to read and write. The Department was in one room off Scotland Yard in London and he always said the detectives went through his room to get to the pub. He was there

*Tony Lessware forking up bales of hay to George Aggett, at Wray Barton,
Moretonhampstead, Devon, 1950s.*

when the first veterinarian was taken on to do something about the problem of glanders in horses. In those days if one was bitten by a horse the wound had to be cauterized with a red hot iron or the result might be fatal. Eventually glanders was wiped out as indeed was rabies, along with tuberculosis in cattle, swine fever, distemper in dogs and other diseases.

I was regarded as slightly 'barmy' when I got down to Devon and started weighing the milk, rationing the feed and bringing the ewes into the barn during 1953–4. We had started baling the straw by then so I made little pens and put the ewes in them as they lambed. I was told I was mad but the others soon followed suit.

The worst part of living and working in the countryside and farming is the townsman's attitude to anything to do with farming. My last job was milking a herd of seventy Friesian cows. I took the job for two reasons. Firstly, I was thoroughly fed up with managing people who didn't know and wouldn't be told how to do things in a changing world and, secondly, I wanted to solve the problem of the let-down of milk which had been bothering me since milking machines were invented. Also, the farm and a very nice cottage looked across to Dartington Woods and for the first time for years I had time on my hands.

I had always kept my fiddle since I learnt for a time when I was a boy. I started experimenting, trying out different thicknesses of bridges and so on. I have now made five fiddles.

The point of all this is, once again, townsfolk's attitudes to countrymen. They look at me and say, 'But you were in farming weren't you? Well how can you do this?' My answer is, 'Anybody who can take a pair of shires and a plough into a 10 acre field, mark out the headland twelve furrows from the hedge, then veer our 17 ft from one side and gather in making 33 ft, veer out again 66 ft from the first and gather in 17 ft each side leaving 33 ft in the middle which is then split, finishing up with one last furrow anything up to a furlong 660 ft long, 9 in wide and straight, will find making and repairing fiddles child's play.'

CHAPTER FIVE

A LINCOLNSHIRE HORSEMAN

Mr J. W. Laughton who progressed from horseman to foreman on a farm in South Humberside between the 1930s and '50s, describes the last days of the horse on the farm. Until horses were displaced by tractors the horseman was the most important worker on the farm.

I was born in 1920 on a farm at Beesby in Lincolnshire. My whole life has been spent living and working on the land.

In 1928 the farmer whom my father worked for left a farm at Biscathorpe (near Louth) and brought us all to a farm at Bonby Top. It was 2 miles down a muddy road from the village of Bonby. It was a pretty rough place, the horse stable in particular and the horses had to stand in big holes. My mother said she was not staying. However, we all decided to make a go of it.

The house was called a Parlour House, all the rooms being on one level. It was very damp and also had lots of black beetles. There was no water supply and water was brought from Bonby in a tank on wheels. In the summer the water was warm and nasty.

The farmer was called Mr Haxby, a proper gentleman but he had not much money so everything had to last as long as possible. He had some beautiful horses and I can still remember their names. If you did not keep hold of them they would run off. One spring, we you did not keep hold of them they would run off. One spring, we had two of them yoked to the corn drill and while the wagoner was filling it, they ran off and smashed the drill to pieces. We had to borrow one as there was no money to buy another.

I started work on the farm when I was fourteen. That winter I had a drove of sheep on turnip land. My job was to keep them well fed and move the fences every day. All the turnips had to be cut up with a machine on two wheels which was called a 'cut-box'. I turned the handle and it cut up the swedes; it took a bit of turning by hand. The job went on come rain, hail or snow as well as Sundays but I enjoyed the work.

My two elder brothers both joined the Army, which meant that we lost the wagoner and the second chap. My father took on two men to do the job; they lived in with us. It was quite a big family

A horseman proudly displays his team, well groomed with shining brasses for a show.
(Mr Barker)

brother and I got promoted to horsemen, he being the wagoner, and we were each paid 11s per week. We had five horses each to look after. My father used to get us up at 5.30 a.m. to feed up and clean out the stables. We came back to the house for a cup of tea and a round of home-made bread and fat bacon. Work started at 6.30 a.m. when we got the horses ready and took them to the fields. The first break was at 9.30 a.m. for a bottle of cold tea (there were no flasks in those days) and bacon in a sandwich. We brought the horses in at 3 p.m. when we had dinner. I might say we were ready for a meal by then!

My mother was a good Methodist and she had to walk about a mile to Chapel. She was very hardworking: she cooked dinner for father at 1 p.m., then the horsemen at 3 p.m. and served tea at about 5.30. She also had to walk to Barton for food which was a round trip of some 7 miles. As the foreman's wife she also had to collect the chicken and duck eggs and send them to market every Thursday. There were five boys and three girls in our family.

After duty in the evenings, we used to walk across to nearby farms to have a talk with other hoschaps (horsemen). Very often it was 2 miles across the fields. There were five farms in our district and we knew all the men. But by 9 p.m. we were back home to bed after feeding the horses which was called 'suppering up'.

During the winter we had the job of threshing the corn out of the stacks. It was a mucky job; my brother and I used to be in the chaff hole. This was all done by steam power in those days with smoke and dust everywhere. The threshing machine consisted of an engine, elevator and drum; the drum separated the corn from the straw and chaff (hence chaff hole). We were all strong lads and were soon able to carry the big chaps of corn, 16 stone of barley, 20 stone of wheat. We considered it to be a better job than the chaff hole. My mother also had to cook dinner for the threshing crew of two men. I don't expect the allowance was overpaid.

Mr Haxby had a herd of breeding Lincoln Red cows and their followers. It found work for us during the winter; we all helped out on wet days. Sometimes when my father was having a difficult calving, we had to help him too. Maybe my brother and I had been to a dance and we would see a light in the crew yard on our return and would have to get stripped off and help to get the calf out. It was a bit cold with your shirt off when it was freezing. My father got 6d per calf; we got nothing. It sometimes took over an hour's work to get the calf out of its mother. We used a light called a hurricane lantern which soon went out if it was windy. We never heard my father use a swear word; he made sure we didn't either.

Harvest time was hard work; the farm men were on ordinary time, while extra help in the form of Irish lads were on piecework. We were working like steam for no extra cash while the Irish lads were on a good rate of pay. There was only one man in the Union in those days.

In due course we purchased a tractor and sold two of my best horses (Bonny and Bute) to help pay for it. I thought it would save a bit of shoe leather if I could drive a tractor so I had a go. It was cold on tractors in those days with no cab or windbreak, but at least we were riding, as against walking behind horses. Anyone who has had four horses in a drag on summer fallows, knows that you go home very tired. On one occasion the vicar called as my brother and I sat down to our 3 p.m. dinner. He gasped when he saw the amount of fat meat and treacle pudding we put away.

We usually had three 30 stone pigs killed for the house – great days on pig's fry and home-made sausage and pork pies. Meat seemed to keep better in those days. The pigs were fed on good barley meal and boiled taters. We also had a cow to milk, so we had plenty of real butter and none of that margarine rubbish.

Sugar beet was grown on the farm. It was all hand work in those early days. Weeds were a problem especially when we chopped out. We went over the crop with a hoe to gap the beet plants about 6 in apart. Sometimes we would go over the crop again later on to clean up the weeds. A good crop was 33,000 plants per acre. The beet was lifted by hand and then carted off to a heap on the roadside

A tractor-drawn cultivator working in Lincolnshire, 1930s. (Mr Wilkinson)

was lifted by hand and then carted off to a heap on the roadside where lorries were filled by hand again and the beet was then delivered to the factory.

Gradually tractors were adapted to take some of the heavy work and more acres were able to be ploughed and also drilled and harrowed etc. Another machine we devised was a truck with the body removed so we could pull implements; we called it the 'horse saver'. We also purchased a farm lorry in 1938. It would carry about 6 tons of corn. I passed my test on it the very first time I took it.

In February 1939 as my two brothers were in the Army I joined up with the Sherwood Foresters. In 1946 on my return home from the War, Mr Haxby had kept me a job so I carried on where I had left off. My first job was to make two hydraulic tipping trailers, the first around this area. It was great to tip a load of manure from the tractor seat just by moving a lever. By this time Ford Major tractors had hydraulic linkage to take a plough or any properly adapted machines; it was sheer magic, especially front end loaders.

My father died in 1945 and was succeeded by my elder brother while I was still in the Army. After 1946 four brothers worked on this farm. It was such a happy working force; everyone had a joke and often a few tricks were played on one another.

Spraying crops started to bring better yields for cereals. It was magic to spray a field of corn and watch all the weeds dying off. Sometimes the corn did too if someone made a mistake! No protective clothes were worn in those days; after a day's spraying

A 1930s Fordson tractor with rubber tyres. (Mr Simmonds)

mentioned combine harvesters. I cannot remember when we first had one; I think in about 1948. The one we had, you had to bag it up, drop the sack on the field and then collect it later.

I was a paid reservist in the Army so I was recalled to the colours in 1950 and sent off to Korea for two years. My job was kept open for me, however, on my return home.

In 1950 all our paraffin lamps were made redundant as electricity came to the village which was a big step forward. As we were short of cash, only the bare essentials were bought. The farmer was the tenant, so just one plug was fitted, costing about £5 per house. By 1952, mains water was in all the villages although some farm cottages were not connected. Money again! However, most of us were connected within two years. There were no bathrooms yet, only the old tin tub in front of the coal fire!

In 1956 I was made foreman and had a house fitted with a bathroom. It was the first one to have a bathroom in the village. It was great to come home from work covered in dust from the corn and to have a bath. Corn driers were terribly dusty machines.

Sadly Mr Haxby had to give up farming, with ill health and age so we all missed him very much.

CHAPTER SIX

EARLY DAYS ON A SHROPSHIRE FARM

*Mr Rochelle was born on a farm near Bridgnorth in Shropshire. He gives a
lovely description of his childhood and youth on that farm, and of life on
the other farms he worked or owned. He also tells of some of the country
characters he knew.*

I was born in the middle room of the old farmhouse at Bromley on
31 December 1912. The first recollection I have is of lying in that
old room and looking up at the high ceiling where there were three
staples embedded. I often used to wonder what they were for. I
learned later that an old man who was bedridden in that room had
a set of pulley blocks attached to them enabling him to pull himself
up in bed unaided.

Bromley Farmhouse is a grand old house in which to rear a
family. I recall the fun we had as children riding up and down the
long passages on our scooters at Christmas time. My first school
days were spent in a small school run by a Mrs Cunnington. My
sister Mary and I used to walk 3 miles to school and back every day,
which was no small feat for a boy of seven, but I am sure it was
good for me. I remember being sent off to school on a winter's
morning in a coat made out of an army blanket which was very
warm and practical. I think my mother had a job to make ends

meet with such a large family, as farming was a very unrewarding profession in those days.

It was when I was about nine years old that I had my first ride in a motor car. My mother saved up the money from her eggs and summoned the garage proprietor who owned the garage in low town. He duly arrived on Saturday morning to take us to Stourbridge to visit my half-brother Walter, who was married and worked at Barclays Bank.

The old Ford was a model T with a big highly polished radiator and two leather straps running from the front wings to the windscreen to support it. The seats were all open and exposed to wind and weather and we all piled in and sped off up the road at a great speed. It would have been 25 mph, which seemed very fast to us as we were used to jogging along with the old pony and trap. I remember my mother holding her hat on with one hand and holding on to the seat with the other as we sped up the Stourbridge straight. The journey seemed endless and I never expected to find our way back. I had never been further than Bridgnorth before, however, we did eventually get back safe and sound after this hair-raising trip abroad.

I was about eleven when I was sent to the Blue Coat School in high town. My mother bought me a second-hand cycle for 30s (£1.50); it was a Rover and had a badge with a Viking's head on, the same as the Rover car, for which I have always had a liking. The headmaster, Mr Blakemore, was a real terror and ruled the school with a stick. One day he made two boys bend down in front of the class and thrashed them all round the room with the dust flying off their backs. This was for a crime they had committed out of school – they had turned the tap of a milk cart on and let all the milk run down the drain. There were no milk bottles in those days, and the milk was measured out of a churn with a pint measure straight into the housewives' jugs. He gave me a couple of strokes one day for not being able to spell. Needless to say, it did no good; if you cannot teach a child by persuasion it's no use trying to knock it into him. I think he used to get on the drink at weekends and take it out on us boys on Monday. I was never any good at school and was always at the bottom of the class. Some boys who were there were very bright and good at figures and have spent all their lives at a desk pushing a pen, so I consider I have led a much more fruitful and rewarding life. I left school on my fourteenth birthday, not having learned much.

My mother used to give me 1s (5p) to put into the school savings bank when I was at the Blue Coat School and as a consequence I had the princely sum of £7 when I left. With this I bought my first pig, who eventually gave birth to eleven piglets on the eleventh day of the eleventh month at 11 a.m. in the morning. They did very well and I sold them to my brother Jack for £22 which made me a very rich lad for those days. This was the cause of my buying my first motor bike, a Dunelt two-stroke capable of the fantastic speed of 60 mph. This was the worry of my mother's life as my brother Leslie had met with a fatal accident on a Norton at the age of twenty-seven.

I worked on the farm at home for a while after leaving school, for a wage of 7s 6d (37p) a week. Needless to say, I didn't do much and spent most of my time catching moles and rabbits to supplement my meagre wage. There was very little discipline as my father was old and crippled with rheumatism.

It was a great shock to me when my mother arranged for me to go to work for my uncle at Westwood Farm where there was much more discipline. I was put to work with the men at swede cutting on a frosty morning. This seemed very hard to me at the time, but I have no doubt it did me good. It was here I was introduced to my first tractor, a 1925 Fordson, which was capable of pulling a two-furrow plough and ploughing 2 acres a day, which was a big improvement on the old horses which I was used to plodding along behind.

While I was at Westwood my father died at the age of seventy-four, leaving me without father or mother at the age of seventeen and without any money or a steady job, as my earnings at Westwood were even more meagre than they had been at home. My uncle was very ill with cancer and lingered on for two years. I used to drive him about in his new Austin but I was never very happy there and when he died I left to go and live at Nordley with my sister Mary who was newly married. I drove a lorry for my brother-in-law. I led a very carefree life with them and was very happy although I was still receiving a very small wage. I was able to keep a few pigs and make a bit this way. In addition I used to get a few tips off the farmers whose stock we transported. The wages seem very small compared with today, but it must be remembered that things were very bad in those days. Farm workers were only getting 35s (£1.75) a week to keep their families on, but they always had a good fat pig in the sty and a well-stocked garden, consequently they were never short of a good lump of bacon and potatoes, and most of them lived on this, and bread and cheese. Their cottages were very poor and had no sanitation or running water. On the whole their needs were small but in spite of this I think they were happier than the workers of today.

Farmers too, were very hard up. I remember taking a ton of potatoes to Wolverhampton market and receiving only 30s for them. Most farmers were heavily in debt and indeed many were going bankrupt. My father owed £750 in rent arrears when he died. My brother took over the farm and had to borrow a large amount to carry on; this was a great handicap to him for many years but he did eventually get things straight, which was a credit to him since it was not a very good farm. It was very sandy and burned up in a dry summer.

I didn't really take much interest in girls in those days as my chief love was the motor bike and any money I had to spare went on this. I only had second-hand ones that were virtually worn out before I had them, but I got a lot of fun out of making do and mending as I have always had an inkling for mechanics.

Charley Powell at Rindleford Mill used to sharpen the stones and he had three sets of stones, two in work and one being sharpened. The flints would fly as he chipped away and would become embedded in his hands which looked as though they were tattooed. He always wore glasses to protect his eyes. He also owned a set of threshing tackle. It would take six strong horses in line astern to pull the engine up the field to Woodside. It was always a big event for us children when the tackle arrived. It was my job to clean the chaff from under the box, the dirtiest job there was. The wagoners were always sent to town to fetch the coal the day before – it cost £1 a ton in those days. One old wagoner named Pugh would always come back the worse for drink; how he ever afforded it I do not know. Beer was 6d a pint then, and twice as strong as today.

At Rindleford there was an old blacksmith's shop and as children we spent many hours watching the blacksmith. The sparks would fly from his hammer as he shaped the horseshoes on his anvil. I can still smell the burning horn as he applied the red-hot shoe to the horse's foot; he must have worked very long hours as I could hear his hammer clanging on the anvil as I lay in bed at Bromley. I could also hear the old mill wheel turning; this would lull me to sleep on summer evenings. There was also a carpenter and wheelwright shop next door to the smithy where Mr Turner used to carry on his thriving business making harvest wagons etc.

I became very friendly with my cousin, Tom Craig, about this time. He had an Alvis Firefly car which was about the smartest car in the district then. We always went places together in this pale blue sports saloon; she was a lovely car and very fast for those days. Tom was always much better off than us and seemed to have no end of money to spend. It was while he was driving in this car one day, that he picked up a party of girl hitchhikers, one of which was Edna Mort who afterwards became his wife. While Tom and Edna were courting, I used to go along to Bilston with them and was introduced to several of Edna's friends, and I went with a girl called Cora for some time.

It was at about this time that my brother-in-law, Reg Rivers, and my sister Mary with whom I lived at that time, took over the tenancy of St James Farm on the outskirts of Bridgnorth. St James was then a farm of some 200 acres. I was then working for Reg full-time driving his lorry and helping on the farm. There was then a small cottage joined to St James House. It was a very quaint little half-timbered dwelling with two up and two down; it had gas and sanitation, which was something I had never had before. He offered me this rent free and a wage of £2 a week; needless to say, I jumped at the chance – there were millions of unemployed at that time. I saw a dole queue 100 yd long and six deep waiting for their paltry 15s (75p) a week. If there was a job vacant there would be a couple of hundred waiting at the door on a Monday morning and some would have been there all night.

Reg offered me the tenancy of 27 acres of pasture at Danesford when I was married. I had no capital to stock it at that time, so I turned to my cousin Tom Craig again as he seemed to be the only one to have any money. He loaned me £200 without any security at all, a thing that not many would do at that uncertain time. It was then that I made one of the biggest mistakes of my farming career. I bought several old cows with calves and turned them out to single suckle. By autumn the cows were thin and old; this is not a good combination to start a hard winter, especially without adequate building and food. Consequently I lost three by the spring. This left me down £100 in twelve months, so the only thing I could do was to start milking the remainder and hope to pull round this way.

It was at this time that I had a disagreement with Reg who had a very hasty temper and he told me to look for another job. I heard that my brother Ern had a cottage vacant at Woodside, so we went up to see it one sunny Sunday in March and fell in love with it right away. He gave us the chance of it with a part-time job on Bromley Farm, driving his tractor, with a wage of £1 a week. This I jumped at, although it meant me working twelve hours a day. I travelled from Woodside to Danesford night and morning, still on my old Levis and milked six cows by hand, working at Bromley from nine to five. I carried on like this for the next few years gradually working up a small herd of good cows, and at the same time raising some store cattle.

At Woodside the house we were in had an old grate; on one side there was a small boiler that heated 2 gallons of water. This and a large kettle were the only means we had of heating water. We bathed our daughters in front of the fire each evening in an old tin bath and when we wanted a tub ourselves we retired into the outside wash-house where we had a boiler that held 20 gallons. It took an hour to heat this; we used wood for most of the fuel. In spite of there being no electricity or water laid on we had oil lamps and went to bed with a candle. The water we carried from a well in the garden, which was well stocked with crawling things but they never seemed to do us any harm. I think we were healthier then than now. The lavatory too was a little wooden affair at the bottom of the garden.

It was after we had been at Woodside for twelve months that our first daughter Jill was born. I remember that night very well. It was about midnight on the night of 23 January; there was very deep snow and hard frost when she decided it was time to arrive. I had no vehicle at that time that was capable of carrying a woman in Bet's state of health, so I walked the mile to Bromley with a hot water bottle under my coat and put its contents into the radiator of Ern's old Austin car, which was not licenced or insured and steamed off to the hospital at Bridgnorth. Afterwards I returned the car to its shed and no one was aware it had been out. Jill arrived before morning, all pink and crinkly. It was two years before our second daughter Sally decided she would like to arrive in this lovely world; she chose a more pleasant time of year to appear, on 8 July.

About this time I decided to have a go at growing peas as I was getting rather fed up with milking cows twice a day, seven days a week. I lashed out rather drastically and planted 6½ acres all at once. This was my lucky day for I made a profit of £500. This really put me on my feet and gave me some working capital; this does not sound much today but it was a considerable sum in those days.

I was now farming 62 acres at Danesford and doing quite a lot of cattle dealing. I sold thirty cattle at one time to make another profit of £500. I then decided to go out of milking and build a bungalow at Danesford. I was lucky to be able to buy 1½ acres of land off my landlady, Miss Owen, and so after a good deal of trouble with permits and planning permission, we set about the building of Greenacres. This was a big expenditure and took all my available capital; in all it took £3,000 to complete. I never regretted building Greenacres and I think it was one of the best investments I ever made, although we were sad to leave Woodside where we had spent fourteen very happy years.

We were now doing all our farming by tractor and most of the old farm horses had gone for meat during the war. I had now given up milking and bought five Wessex gilts and started pig breeding while continuing with cattle dealing. I did very well at both these enterprises over the next few years and worked up a nice bit of capital.

Of the animals I have known over the years, I suppose dogs come to my mind first. When I was a boy at Bromley, my brother Les had a dog called Pop. He was a long-haired blue and grey sheep-dog with a wall eye. He was a real friend to all the family, but a great enemy of the game keepers. If we were walking with him and happened to run into the keeper, he would show his disapproval by raising his hackles and growling, much to the keeper's annoyance. He was a very faithful old dog and a loyal friend, but not much good at his work and he was also shy of the gun. I recall the day I was collecting chestnuts in High Rock Coppice with Pop. Then the keeper, W. Garat, a man who was much disliked by all, and especially by me, came along and ordered me off. I said to Pop, 'See him off Boy', and he responded by showing his fangs and growling. Garat replied by threatening to shoot him. He reported me to the head keeper but nothing ever came of it. Alas, the old dog ended his days at the wrong end of a gun; he was shot while rabbiting, which was his favourite pastime.

Several dogs have come and gone in my lifetime, but the ones that stay uppermost in my memory are my two recent ones, Bob and

Bruce. Bob was a pure-bred black Labrador and a very good friend to us all. He was especially attached to my daughter, Jill. Alas, he met a very sad end when he went to sleep under a lorry that was loading on the farm, which ran over him when it started off.

Bruce was a Labrador–Spaniel cross who was much addicted to going courting. He would go miles looking for a girlfriend, but unfortunately he could never find his way back home and used to end up at the police station. I think he became more well known to the police than any dog in the district. He got to know his way to the station and would go there of his own accord when he got tired of patrolling the town, and would lie down by the radiator and wait for me to pick him up. When I was making enquiries about him at the desk, he would hear my voice, and I would then hear his tail thumping on the boarded floor in the next room. I would pay the few shillings and bail him out. Alas, he too came to a sticky end at Danesford. He was run over on the road one cold frosty morning when he was accompanying me to feed the pigs in the dark. Thus ended a beautiful friendship. Both these friends lie under my lawn and are often in my thoughts. Bruce's sad end so upset me, in fact, that I vowed never to have another dog while I lived at Danesford, and nor have I!

Pigs have played quite an important part in my life, right from the time I left school until I was sixty. Some of the breeding sows I have had have become real friends. It is surprising how intelligent some of them are. I once had a sow called Stumpy that could open any door I had and she became such a nuisance that I had to get rid of her. She was very clever and would follow me around like a dog. On hot days she would get into the water tank for a bath. But the pig that stands out most in my memory is the one I had when I left school. She made me a real good profit in her time. I once had ten sows at Danesford that reared me 125 pigs in six months and I sold them for £5 each, £625. Stumpy was one of these sows. I often wonder if this was a record for those days, it would certainly take a lot of beating.

During the first twenty-five years of my life, horses also played a very important part in my work, but never much for pleasure. The first one I knew was the pony we had at Bromley, called Jerry. He was very fat and lazy, he used to trundle around the farm with us in the old tub; we sometimes used to ride him too, but he was so fat that we had difficulty straddling his back. When he died my mother would not have him sent to the 'knackers' but insisted on him being buried on the farm. I remember I had the job of digging his grave, which was no mean task for a boy of fourteen. Old Madam, the cart-horse, and her daughter Blossom were two others I recall and I spent many days walking behind them. When I first came to Danesford the only power I had on the land was an old white horse called Captain, who served me faithfully for several years. Alas, he became lame and as meat was in very short supply during the war, he had to go the same way as many more good horses went at the time. I received £40 for him, which was a lot of money in those days. I did my ploughing with him and a borrowed horse and a single furrow plough. I was never as fond of horses as some farmers were and I was glad when I could afford an old Fordson tractor to take their place.

An old couple that I call to mind were named Merrie. They lived in a little cottage in the high rock coppice. The old lady had lived in the district all her life, she was the local midwife and was responsible for bringing all my mother's children into this world, including myself. She was a very fat old lady and when she was called to a case it was always customary to get a case of stout in for she would not go up the stairs until she had had a pint. She would sit and sip it very slowly in spite of the pleas for her help from her patient. She would say, 'All in good time my dear, all in good time'. Her name was Mrs Payne at this time and very appropriate too; her first husband must have died quite young, for I never knew him. She was about seventy when she married her second husband whose name was Will Merrie. He must have been seventy-two for he was drawing his pension and working at Bromley part-time. He was a real old character with snow-white side whiskers and he always wore cord trousers with a strap below the knee. I worked many days with him; his favourite job was hedge laying and he taught me the art of pleaching a hedge [entwining the branches], but I was never anywhere in his class.

Another couple I can remember were Mr and Mrs Sam Jones who lived in a cottage in Bromley. He also worked on the farm. Sam was a very tall man of about 6 ft 5 in, he had very big feet and walked with a stoop. Will and he were always at loggerheads; I once heard Will say to him, 'You'd be a tall man Sam if you hadn't got so much turned up at the bottom.' There was always great rivalry between them over hedge laying, each thinking he was better than the other. I once heard Sam say to Will, 'You'n killed that bloddy hedge, Will.' There was no doubt Will was the better hedge layer, although he was a bit rough. Once when we had a load of grain to unload up on to a high stack we were debating who should be the pitcher, when it was suggested that the tallest man should have the job. Sam said, 'I expect I be the shortest of the four on yer.' When we were making hay during the war and there were a lot of aeroplanes about, he would look up at the sky and say, 'We um bound to have some rain before long with all these old airyplanes a buzzing about.' His wife used to assist the old undertaker in his duties and when Sam died she was heard to say, 'Ah he was a lovely corpse.' I recall his skin was very brown and wrinkled like old parchment. He used to smoke a very short old pipe, which he called his 'nose warmer'.

There was another old man called Bodger who lived with his two sons, Bob and Alf, in an old black and white cottage with a thatched roof. The old man got a living by catching moles and making pegs for the housewives of the village. His two sons worked on the land. Bodger was also an amateur vet. One lad who lived down the Batch had a pet dog called Caesar that was grossly over-fed. He finally got so fat that he would not eat at all and he said to Bodger one day, 'I wish you could do something for my dog, he won't eat.' To which Bodger replied, 'Let me have him for a week man; I'll cure him.' He did; he tied him to his apple tree for a week with plenty of water and no food. When he returned him to his owner he was half the weight and ravenously hungry. The lad was delighted and gave him 12s (60p); he said it was the easiest 12s he ever earned.

I was a boy of about eight when his son Alf went raving mad one hot summer's day; he paraded up and down the village howling like a dog. They sent for the police and the black maria, which was horse-drawn then, and proceeded to round him up. This took several hours as he had taken to the woods by then. This put the fear of God into me and I can still hear his terrible howling in holly bush coppice to this day. They finally did catch him and he was taken away never to return. Bodger's other son Bob was a crony of my father's and used to carry drink to him from Bridgnorth.

My father used to disappear every evening at about 10 p.m. So one evening I decided to follow him. He disappeared into Bob's cottage and I crept up and looked through the window; they were sitting one each side of the fireplace drinking whisky. The room was very sparsely furnished with an old table and wooden chairs, there was no carpet on the stone flag floor and no curtains at the windows and the only means of light was an old oil lamp on the table with a soot covered glass. A log fire was burning in the old cast-iron grate, mole skins were nailed to boards around the room to dry and a loaf of bread and some cheese were on the table along with all the dirty crocks. I don't think he ever washed them; he himself was always very dirty and uncared for. I don't think he ever washed himself or his clothes, he stunk to high heaven and was reputed to be lousy, but in spite of all this he lived to a ripe old age.

Another two old men I call to mind were the two Davies brothers, who were known locally as the Jacky brothers. As far as I knew they never had a house but used to sleep in the farm buildings around the district. They never did much work but used to scrounge food off the farmers' wives and collect rags which they sold in Bridgnorth. If they were given an old overcoat they would wear it themselves over the top of the ones they had already got. I have seen them with as many as four on; they would scarcely be able to walk for the weight. They sported no buttons but each coat would be tied up with binder twine. At Christmas time they would go carol singing. Jack would sing while his younger brother Fred would play the mouth organ. Jack was once heard to say, 'I've got 500 acres of carol singing to do this year.' He was once summonsed for trying to obtain money by false pretences and was duly taken over to the Town Hall. When he arrived he had on his usual four coats, two pairs of trousers and various old scarves. After he had left the court room the police were seen going around the witness box with disinfectant spray.

They stayed in the building at Woodside all one winter during the war and slept up there, being in front of the cattle where it was warm. We were very fed up with them and their dirty habits, so I said to them one morning, 'Captain Brockbank of E Division Home Guard was asking me where he could find you chaps, he wants to enlist you.' We didn't see them again for at least six months; I heard they had gone over the other side of the river to bless the farmers there with their company. At one time in their lives they had a donkey and cart in which they collected rags and bones about the town. When the donkey died, Fred, who was much younger than Jack, used to pull the cart himself. He was giving Jack a ride along Under Hill Street one hot day, until they came to New Road, when Fred got tired and threw the shafts up in the air and deposited Jack on his back in the middle of the road.

Old Jim Cureton was another old character I knew. It was in 1940 that he first bestowed himself upon me. It was October time and I had 5 acres of sugar beet to be pulled by hand. There were no machines in those days. Along came old Jim with his pack on his back asking for beet pulling. I set him my 5 acres and he settled himself down in my shed with an old oil stove and plenty of straw for his bed. It was not until he had his first sub that I discovered his weakness; he came back from town as drunk as a lord and very objectionable. But in spite of this weakness he was a real gentleman and returned for fourteen years to pull my beet which he did very efficiently. I recall saying to him one day, 'Why do you go to town up the river side Jim?'. Jim replied, 'So as I will come to the grocer's shop before the pub.' He could not go past the pub with £1 in his pocket and once in, he would spend every penny he had and come back without any food for the remainder of the week.

The last time he came he arrived a month late without letting me know he was coming, by which time I had let it to a younger man. Jim was getting old by now, I gave him £1 for a drink and the last I heard of him, he was blind drunk asleep under a hedge in Oldbury. I always like to think of him as 'Gentleman Jim', for this I think he was. I once heard that he came from a good old and respected farming family. My brother-in-law Reg Rivers once found him down in the road on St James's corner and put him to sleep in the barn with his two Labrador dogs, Ben and Bella, who kept watch over him through the night. They became firm friends after this and he always went and had a word with them when passing. The police had him inside jail several times and fined him 10s (50p). They got tired of this, however, and after a while they used to bring him down to Danesford and dump him in my shed. He was in such a terrible state one night that they would not have him in their car, so they hired Jack Gamond with his 1 ton truck to transport him back and made him pay for the hire, a fee of 5s (25p). He always respected me when he was sober and called me 'Sir' and my wife 'M'am', but when he was drunk he called me by my Christian name. I always tried to avoid him when he was in that state as he became very nauseating.

When my father first went to Bromley, there were two old people who lived in the big house down the Batch. They told him a story about a box of gold that was buried somewhere there. He once repeated a ditty to me that went something like this. 'In a valley between two fields there lies a box of gold concealed', and it went on to say '. . . three fields down from the crossroads on the went on to say '. . . three fields down from the crossroads on the Wolverhampton Road', but I cannot remember the rest of it. This would have been in the year 1800 approximately. This was the valley that is on the Bromley or north side of the Burcot road and never gets cultivated. I once did try to plough it but got bogged down with the tractor. I wonder if there really is any gold there. The old man that related this story to my father was later found hanged from a beam in the back kitchen of his house, which since then is reputed to be haunted. My daughter Jill once slept there and said when she woke in the night, there was someone standing by her bed. I have heard several stories of things being seen in this house but have never been able to confirm them. It is certainly a

A group of haymakers having a break after loading the wagon, 1920s. Note the large rake in the foreground. This photograph was taken in Shropshire and includes the father of Mr Tart of Wellington.

79

Autumn 1978

This fragrant earth beneath my feet.
This stormy path, this fiery street.
This spongy sod of turf and peat.
This land of ours, this land of flowers.
This land I've gleaned a living from,
This land I've ploughed and sown and reaped.
This land wherein my fathers sleep.
This England!
I've seen the sun go down sublime,
I've seen the lightning strike the pine,
I've helped the miller grind his corn,
Where willows weep on frosty morn,
I've lived on wholemeal from his stone,
But now I walk his road alone.
For now he lies beneath a stone in a graveyard on the hills,
I've helped the smithy blast and strike,
And give new life to harrow spike,
He too has gone to graveyard lot,
With iron cross to mark the spot.
I have no part this time to play,
In farming scene this autumn day.
Some sixty falls have gone my way,
And now I sit and dream all day.
I dream of days that now are gone,
And think of pleasant days to come.
Of children playing in the sun,
Of cosy hearth with blazing log,
And walking with my favourite dog.
And watch kingfishers darting by,
And hovering hawk in azure sky.
And when at last I've had my lot,
What will I have to mark my plot.
An upturned plough, a pike or two.

CHAPTER SEVEN

MARKET GARDENING IN ESSEX

Mr Frederick Barker tells the story of work and life on a small farm at Wanstead. He describes the methods used in the growing and marketing of vegetables and fruit and also makes interesting comparisons between the 1930s and the present day.

I was born on 25 November 1915 at Wanstead, 7 miles northeast of London. It was on a farm of about 150 acres, 60 of which were in grass or flooded land while the other 90 produced vegetables.

My grandfather, something over a hundred years ago, ran away from home in Suffolk. His father was a publican and his stepmother he found rather difficult. He earned his living to start with by carting stable manure from the London stables to the market gardens in the Kingston, Wimbledon and Twickenham areas. He fell in love with a farmer's daughter but the farmer wouldn't allow his daughter to marry a dung carter, so he set him up on a small piece of ground in Mitcham. They they had five children, of which my father was the eldest. My father moved to Wanstead in about 1910 onto the farm where I was born.

Grandfather used to sell his own produce in Covent Garden. We had a stand there right up to 1985–6 and my father was a devoted Covent Garden salesman of his own produce. So a typical day in his life would be leaving home at 8 p.m. in the evening from Wanstead and catching a train to Covent Garden where he would sleep, just by Bow Street police station. He would then get up in the morning at about 2 a.m. and sell his produce. Afterwards, he would catch a train and be home by about 12 noon. He would just have a quick look at the farm and then have lunch. In the afternoon he would have a snooze and then he would come out and have another look at the farm prior to his evening meal and going back to market again. His evening meal was really tea, we had our main meal at midday and not a cooked one in the evening. He kept this up for many years, even when we moved. It wasn't till much later in life that we altered our marketing system.

Horses used to take the produce from Wanstead to Covent Garden, which was not very far – only about 8 or 9 miles I suppose. They stopped at Stratford and had a drink while the wagoner was still asleep on the rack in the front of the wagon. We had a Thorneycroft lorry on solid tyres, that was in about 1928 I suppose, and that stood us in fairly good stead. It could carry about 4 or 5 tons.

On this 100 acre farm, 90 acres were devoted to vegetables, including lettuces, both round and cos, radishes, rhubarb, marrows, parsnips, beetroot, leeks, spring onions, spinach and potatoes. They all required a lot of hand labour and we also had further regular people who lived at Wanstead and Woodford who came to work for us.

In 1930, when I was only fifteen, father moved to Southfleet, which is 22 miles east of London and about 2 or 3 miles south of the Thames. Here, he came on to a 500 acre farm with poor soil, and a lot of chalk and flint. It was quite a different job and I think misguidedly he tried to grow all the same crops. Mind you, he succeeded and kept going when a lot of people didn't. Perhaps the second war helped him then.

I left school in 1933 and my first job was cutting lettuce, bagging spring greens, and looking after a gang of women who were picking potatoes and parsnips by hand. I had to do quite a bit of the drilling with an 8 ft wide Suffolk drill pulled by two horses. One man would lead the horses, myself holding the drill straight and a man behind seeing that the seed was running alright. I also bunched rhubarb in the shed and used to help load the lorries. Bunching rhubarb, I thought, was rather fun; five dozen bunches an hour was a regular job. Not done now, it is all sold loose, I think. Another thing we had was cold frames, we just called them lights. We used them for raising lettuce plants. Father was very particular about those and I must admit that when I took over later on, I abandoned them altogether, because I found that we couldn't get lettuce really early in the season. They were only second early and came in with the flood of everybody else's lettuce. We were better off without them.

The hours we worked before the Second World War were 7 a.m. until 5 p.m. with no break for breakfast; no one liked that. In the summer time we worked from 6 a.m. until 6 p.m. with half-an-hour for breakfast and an hour for lunch. Lots of hand tools were used in those days. We had hoeing people who came down from Bedfordshire regularly every year; four or five men would come down and lodge with our men. They hoed the parsnips, the spring onions and the harvest onions.

Men's wages were 8¼d (3p) an hour, but I think we paid 8½d and women were on 6d (2½p) an hour. We reckoned that if the men were on piecework they ought to earn 1s (5p) an hour and the women about 9d (3½p). Of course, there was no inflation from 1924 until 1936 and so you knew exactly what wages you were going to pay each year. It seems strange now that every year everyone automatically expects a rise in wages.

Father was the boss and we had a foreman on the farm here at Southfleet; he was paid £4 a week. Father did quite a bit of work and he still carried on this market job. He left in the evening and caught a train and went to London and came back the next day. During the war, when the raids were on, he still went to Covent

Garden every day but he used to go on the lorry instead. All our produce went to Covent Garden; there would be four or five loads of it from our two farms. It was sold to retailers, wholesalers, hotels, and catering suppliers. Wednesday was what was called a 'country day' when people came up from the country and secondary wholesalers would buy produce; that was a different market altogether.

We soon had a couple of Caterpillar tractors. We ran the farm with just two small-wheeled tractors, Internationals, and sixteen chestnut Suffolk horses. One of the first things my father did when he came to Southfleet was to have three horses to pull a plough. It was the Kent balanced plough using three instead of four, which all our neighbours used. A boy would lead the horses with one man on the plough. We had three horses abreast and one man, the ploughman, managed them by himself.

There has been no real trade union problem. A few years ago we wished to alter our cropping programme, which meant that we didn't want a small gang of women anymore. We called in the secretary for the trade union, the county secretary, and asked him to tackle the job and it was handled quite amicably.

I got married in 1941 during the war, and very wisely, I think, my father moved out of the farmhouse, just a couple of miles away. I became responsible for all the day-to-day things but he still dealt with the major items. I was foreman on the farm then and father was pretty fussy about the way all the jobs were done. Every night I had a large sheet of paper and wrote down the jobs that had to be done; I usually started at the top with the teams of horses, allocating the different horses to the different jobs. It may not seem sense now, but of course, certain horses would put one foot in front of the other quite neatly and they could walk up a row of cabbages, whereas others were much more spreadfooted and couldn't do so without causing damage. We would have a frisky horse that couldn't be put with a certain person for carting because it didn't like the noise in the yard, or whatever it may be. So we set down the horses and the teams and the men on their jobs followed by the ordinary manual workers who would be hoeing or digging or planting. After that two or three gangs of women would usually be marketing, packing lettuce, cutting greens, pulling spring onions, bunching radishes etc. Then, of course, there was the market load itself. The aim at the end of the day was to get the load ready for the markets.

Selling was still done through Covent Garden. I suppose it was thirty years ago when supermarkets decided to take fresh produce and we supplied them from our stand in Covent Garden. As the supermarkets became more demanding, we delivered to them and now, during the last twenty years, we have done all we can to supply exactly what they want and deliver it when they want it. Our business has grown rapidly in recent years from the demands of supermarkets.

The main overall difference today in the workforce on the farm, is that we used to have a large labour force of men and women who were producing the crop, planting, hoeing, hand weeding and singling. We also had another group of people for marketing and harvesting it. Now, you can reckon there is no hand labour at all in producing the crops that we grow, except for thinning out the cabbage. We have sprays which sort out all the weeds and precision seeding drills which will put two seeds down every foot or two feet or however wide you want them and they just have to be singled. We make no attempt on our poor soil to compete with Lincolnshire and Cambridgeshire where marketing is mechanized. We couldn't use a potato harvester and we couldn't grow carrots, so we specialize in crops that need hand labour for harvesting, crops such as lettuce, spring onions, cutting cabbage, parsley, radishes, in fact most of the crops that are not mechanically harvested.

The land here is hard and difficult to cultivate. We used the horses to harrow and roll the land in order to get a season for the seed to get in but it was just like a rock and very difficult indeed; the resulting crops were very poor. Today there are rotary harrows which can break up the soil about 8 or 10 in deep. We can get very good crops indeed, even regular crops. All the farms are irrigated and so that helps too.

Precision seeding not only saves seed but means that you have the right number of plants. This saves a lot of hoeing, singling and setting out. Spraying, of course, is a great help, in spite of what all the conservationists say. I still think there is a place for sprays in order to get the perfect crop.

Modual plants, that means little seedlings, in little soil blocks are grown elsewhere. We have had them imported from Holland but we have also bought them from the north and the west of England. We plant these regularly, especially lettuce and cabbage. The supermarkets have forced us into pre-packing so we now have quite a sizeable pack house with about thirty or forty people packing spring greens, wrapping cabbage, swedes, and washing and packing spring onions and radishes. This is, of course, a major change.

There was a lot of unemployment from 1930 to 1940 so it was not difficult to get casual labour. There was plenty of casual labour available from the Chatham Dockyard. During the period 1940 to 1950 we had the Women's Land Army and from 1950 onwards we employed students, many from Scandinavia. In the last twenty years or so we have had Indian women who live in Gravesend, and who come from the Punjab.

Today we are able to take students more regularly at the pack house because there is a constant demand for produce right through the year from the supermarkets. In my early days there was much less work in the winter so it was not economical to employ a student. Wages are now paid mainly by bank transfer, whereas men and women used to queue up at the office. Over thirty years ago I started having a farm outing at Christmas time and we went either to a theatre or to something like the Royal Mews, one of the cathedrals or a trip round a factory. We visited two or three factories and several historic places. In time the people for whom we really wanted the outings, that is our key men, became less interested so we then stopped it altogether. In the last few years we have had a staff party which has been a dinner and dance which we usually hold at the beginning of February. This has been most successful. Unfortunately most of the Indian women don't come because they are not accustomed to socialize without their husbands at the same place, as far as I gather. However, all the pack-house women bring their husbands and partners and we get about 170 or 180 people there and have a very good time.

We are only 24 miles from London so we employ many people from London. We did have six village shops some forty or fifty years ago; now we have only two. We have a builder's yard and a butcher's shop and yard in the village and sadly these will probably close down in due course because there is no family to take them on. We have kept all the cottages at my own farm and use them all, whereas many other farmers have sold theirs off and they have become owner occupied. I remember we had several council houses in the village, I think there were about 120. I remember one row of houses where there was only one telephone. Now I would have thought that every one of those houses has not only got a telephone but a car standing outside as well. House prices, of course, have changed and completely redundant farm cottages have been done up and sold for very high prices. The church has developed a lot, of course, and the village has got a little bigger and we now have a full congregation every Sunday morning. When there are christenings or special days, we will put out 150 extra chairs and fill the church completely with all ages of people. The Sunday school has just under one hundred children in; it is a very creditable situation.

Some twenty years ago we built a village hall and that has markedly changed the village. The Women's Institute meets there and instead of having a small meeting in one of our offices, it now has a membership of 60 or 80. The Gardeners' Society had its dinner recently and there were 90 there. The Flower Arrangers are over subscribed at 100 plus and then there are two cricket clubs. There is also a ladies discussion evening and a men's club. The village is quite a lively village. It also has the advantage of not being a through village.

The main change in cropping, I suppose, since the 1930s is that the village still grows vegetables. We, ourselves, are mainly big vegetable growers and other farmers in the village also grow vegetables while all the orchards have been grassed over. There was a lot of fruit and hops in the village at one time, but today there is only one farm growing hops instead of five. None of the farms keep stock, not even one chicken. Originally each farm used to have a yard for fattening cattle and most of them had a flock of sheep. Today one farm is almost entirely corn.

What was a typical working day? In the 1930s on the vegetable farm, the lettuce had to be cut all through the summer; they were always cut first thing in the morning. We usually had four or five men cutting lettuce and twice that number of women packing them at the back. They would all finish at about 9 a.m. when the men were almost certain to go hoeing, using short-handled hoes. They would be hoeing lettuce, spinach, harvest onions or parsnips or they would thin out beetroot. The women might also be hoeing, or they would weed, or pull spring onions or rhubarb for the men to bunch. Then there might be a day when they would plough up parsnips and then load them up into the carts in the afternoon. A plough would go up and down the field lifting the parsnips, then the ten or twelve men or women spread out along the row would pick them up and put them into heaps.

After dinner the horses that were pulling the plough would change over into carts and cart the parsnips into the shed where they were put into a heap. Here the dirt would be rubbed off and they would be put into bags or boxes for market. The wagoners almost always had the job for the whole day: they would either be ploughing, harrowing or drilling all day. In fact, the art of laying out the work for the workers was to give them as little moving about from field to field as possible as they would have to walk which took time and cost money.

There is no doubt that the crops grown now are far superior to those that were grown fifty to eighty years ago. The marketing and presentation is also much improved. Customers today would not buy now the produce that we used to send up to Covent Garden! The supermarket expects the produce to be fit to put on display, whereas before the war a greengrocer or barrow boy would be prepared to buy a quantity of sub-standard produce and trim it up himself and make it saleable. Sadly there isn't a barrow boy trade any longer.

We still have the same number of markets in London but they are all declining as they have far less produce to handle. Sixty per cent of the fresh produce now goes direct to supermarkets and does not go into the markets at all.

CHAPTER EIGHT

FARMING IN KENT

Mr Robert Body sent me a lengthy document which covered his family's history from the birth of William Body in 1848 to the present time. William's father, Thomas, farmed at Willersham and on his death William took over the farm. In 1884 he moved to Dunstall Farm at Shoreham. Robert Body goes on to describe the methods of farming followed by his family in the late nineteenth and early twentieth centuries. In particular, he describes the work of his father, Harold, who started work in 1890 and continued until 1945.

At Dunstall Farm, hops and corn were grown and grass seed was also grown and sold to farmers wishing to put arable fields down to pasture. Hay and straw were sold to London merchants for retailing to horse owners and on one occasion a load of silage was sent. William, who dealt with that part of the business, called on this particular merchant and found the silage spread all round the yard drying; it was probably the only load of silage ever sent to London horses. In about 1892, there was a National Competition for the best silage produced. Two experts came to Dunstall Farm to judge William Body's silage. He did not win a prize but during a meal one of the judges, on learning about the grass seed production, suggested that a sample should be sent to the Grass Seeds Trials at Hawarden in Cheshire. The following year this was done. The mixture, which probably consisted of Kent Perennial rye grass,

Crested Dog's Tail and Wild White Clover, produced such outstanding notice that the value of Kent Wild White Clover first came to the public notice.

William and Sarah Body had seven sons and six daughters, and it is their third son, Harold whose farming experience we are mainly concerned with. In the late 1890s his father sent him down to Romney Marsh, where he was renting land at Honeychild Manor, Jesson Farm, St Mary's and Plum Tree at Old Romney. It appears that he joined the East Kent Yeomanry in 1896.

Harold Body soon started widening his enterprises. By 1904 he had bought New Romney Windmill. His miller was Tom Weston with Ben Whitehead doing the selling, including a round delivering with horses and van. He lost the tenancy of Honeychild at Michaelmas in 1911. Presumably he fell out with the landlords and for a year lived at Elm Tree House, New Romney.

By Michaelmas the following year Haffenden Farm had been bought and the mill business let to the Carey Brothers who ran the horse buses to Ashford, Folkestone and Rye and who also provided a 'fly' (closed four-wheel carriage) service to New Romney Station.

Haffenden Farm was a good farm of some 220 acres with good stables and other buildings and rather stiff land suitable for an arable farm. There were two four-horse teams each with a wagoner and mate, who every evening, as well as looking after their horses had to chaff enough hay for the next day. One odd heavy horse, a Vanner and a trap horse were also kept. Altogether there were eight to ten men and boys. In summer, when the horses were turned out at night to graze, the horsemen had to scythe enough 'Green Meat' (lucerne or red clover and rye grass) for the horses next day.

The land was steam ploughed as soon as possible using a ploughing set consisting of two engines with 1,200 ft of steel wire rope wound round the drums under the engines' boilers, a five- or six-furrow balance plough, a cultivator, a two-wheeled water barrel with a hand pump and a living van. There were two drivers, a ploughman and his mate and a boy whose most important job was teamaker and cook. There was always a coal fire in the living van. There were five steam plough sets in the Marsh: four Fowlers and one Aveling & Porter. The ploughing was done at around £1 per acre, cultivating at half price. Harold always tipped the foreman well. Every other Saturday the boiler fires were let out so that the caked mud from the ditch water could be washed out. In drought years, when water was short and very muddy, this had to be done weekly; great big encrustations of salt would build up round every plug and manhole in the fire boxes. There was a lead plug in every fire box, and if the water became too hot, or did not circulate properly, the plug would melt and the water would put the fire out. Unless the engines were working along full ditches of water, a man and a pair of horses were fully occupied fetching water and coal.

Winter wheat was the main crop; Victor was the best yielder and Yeoman usually made a shilling or two more. A bearded wheat called Rivetts was occasionally sown in the spring and Red Standard Black winter oats was also grown for the horses who had at least one bushel a week each. Oats were rather liable to shed; in fact, I remember three crops of winter oats grown in succession in the same field and only the first was sown, and the last was not the worst. Some winter barley was sometimes grown and spring barley was the last resort if it was too late to drill anything else. Tic beans, Long Red beans, tares, peas and turnip seed were also grown and a fresh ley of lucerne, red clover and rye grass, in rotation. The Tic beans were for feed or sale, the Long Pods were usually grown on contract, as was the white turnip and swede seed; some peas were on contract and some just for sale. One variety, Harrison's Glory, was sold for the packaging grocery trade, whereas the contract seed was grown for merchants in different parts of the country. White turnip and swede seed was grown from plants up on the hills. The plant grower was paid by the number of acres planted out in the spring; he had to pull the plants and the marsh farmer had to fetch them but not too many at a time so that the plants were fresh. The land for turnip seed was harrowed down and rows 'struck' at eight rows to the rod 2 ft 2 in apart. This was done with a corn drill; it just made a crease so that the planter could follow dibbing the plants at 15 in intervals. Long Pod bean rows were 2 ft apart and the beans dibbed at 6 in intervals with the planter carrying a gallon of seed in a small bag tied to his waist. The turnip plants were firmed by squeezing the soil against the plant with the dibber pushed into the ground an inch or so away – the test was to pull on a leaf, if the leaf broke it was fine. Beans were covered by slouching dirt over the plants with one's feet. The beans were particularly vulnerable to rooks and pigeons after they had sprouted. Long Pod beans could be drilled by having a specially adapted corn drill, but blockages often occurred. Peas were drilled sometimes in wide rows: either ten rows to the rod or sometimes twenty.

A certain amount of Wurtzer seed was sometimes contracted for and planted in wide rows. All these contract seeds were hand hoed and shimmed, and later baulked up, so that they stood up better if there was strong wind. When these crops were in bloom, the merchants sent down men to rough them, that is to pull up any plant that was of another variety or not true to that strain.

White turnip seed, which had a vivid yellow blossom, was the first to be harvested. It was cut in drifts, the faster and more experienced men going first and each man cutting three rows. No. 1 would lay his seed as far to his left as possible. No. 2 did likewise and No. 3 put his on No. 2's row, then No. 4 put his rows of seeds as far as he could to his right as did Nos. 5 and 6. That meant that there was an 8 or 9 ft gap between Nos. 3 and 4. This gap was required when the seed was to be picked up and this pattern was followed right across the field. The seed was cut with seed hooks and the cutter reached forward and grasped as much as he could with his left hand, and by bending the crop forward was able to cut about 15 in high what he held with his left hand, well in front of his hook so that there was little danger of cutting himself. The seed was carefully laid in wodges of three or four handfuls; a week or ten days later the seed would be ripe for threshing. There were two processes: the first was carried out the previous night. It consisted of cleaning a patch about 20 yd square in the middle of the area to be worked on the following day. The seed would either be loaded or laid back on the surrounding seed, then the seed stalks which were largely still standing in the ground were pulled up and checked out of the way, then an area of 36 sq ft was levelled and cleared. The second process was started the next day. The ground was then ready for a 36 ft square cloth to be laid down and stumped tight at the corners. A good quality cloth would weigh 2½ cwt when dry. The nearby seed was then spread by hand on to the cloth and put in a fairly large circle. Then a steady horse was led round and round on this circle of seed pulling a smooth roll with two men following to shake the straw up so that more seed was rolled out each time around. I might add that a sack was always nailed across the shafts to catch any horse droppings. When the seed had been rolled enough, the straw would be forked off the cloth and out of the way. Incidentally, the forkers had to be careful not to make holes in the cloth. Then more unthreshed seed would be put down until there began to build up a lot of seed and seed pods. Hay rakes were used to move the threshings and by a chopping action most of the pods could be separated from the seed, and the pods were then thrown off the cloth. When enough seed had accumulated the seed would be hand sifted (in a 3 ft sieve) and then sacked up. After the area round the cloth had been cleared, a gang would start picking up the rows of seed. Using a horse-drawn wooden sledge about 10 ft by 6 ft lined with a hessian cloth nailed through slats of wood with diagonal ropes lying in the bottom and tied to the corners, the seed would be carefully picked up, a wodge or two at a time. Two or three boys would be in the sledge stomping the turnip seed down so that as much as possible could be loaded. Knees and arms suffered a lot from the rough stalk ends. The sledge when full would be drawn alongside (the right way for the wind), the rolling cloth and all hands available would tip the sledge on to its side, on the cloth, and then, by pulling on the ropes, the sledge would be emptied two or three times so that the seed which had accumulated in the bottom of the cloth would also be got out. The load was spread in a circle and so the job went on. In the meantime the field gang would be loading the next sledge. Sometimes an engine and thresher would be hired but the procedure would be the same except for the horse and roll, and getting the seed off the cloth.

Turnip and swede seed were very vulnerable to the weather when ripening. A heavy rain or strong wind could cause severe losses and it was almost impossible to handle the stuff in a very strong wind. Long Pod beans were always cut by hand using a bagging hook with a crank between the blade and the handle, which was pulled towards one while pushing the stalks away. Sometimes it was easier and quicker to pull the whole plant out of the ground and lay it in wodges, each cutter doing two rows a drift. Most of the Long Pods grown in the Marsh were cut, tied into sheaves and shocked up by 'gypsies' or travellers, usually four sheaves to a shock with the butts upwards, as that was the end where the pods were. The sheaves were tied with cut lengths of binder twine. In a hot period the beans were tied in the morning while the dew was still on them as the bean pods opened up so easily. In fact I remember one year we loaded all the available wagons before breakfast, starting at dawn, then unloading them and getting them ready again during the day. It took three days to clear the beans and so many beans were shelled onto the ground that a gang of children were paid so much a bucket to pick them up.

Beans were always loaded on the wagons and the stack was built with the tips of the sheaves outwards and the butts inward, unlike sheaves of corn. When they were threshed the thresher drum had to be slowed down by changing pulleys to avoid cracking too many beans. Wurtzel seed was planted out like turnips and cut and tied like beans; extreme care had to be used as the seed rubbed off so easily. Wurtzel seed could only be grown in certain areas because of cross-pollination and it took some time after cutting to ripen thoroughly. It was usually stacked with air channels through the stack, using hurdles in an inverted V formation.

Peas, the short strawed varieties, were always cut by hand as the pods were so close to the ground. A swap was used for this; this was an L-shaped tool with a 15 in blade. It was part of an old scythe with about a 3 ft handle and a leather loop at the top and a scythe handle grip about a foot down. The man's forearm went through the loop and the peas were lifted up and rolled back with a right-angled hook stick in the pea cutter's other hand. The cut peas were rolled into 18 in rolls. Peas could shatter very easily so care had to be taken. The wodges of peas had to be turned so that they dried through. Long strawed peas could often be cut with a mower, perhaps one way only. The men would follow the mower rolling the peas up and lifting them back out of the way of the mower's next swathe. About twenty pea growers began to stack peas on tripods to let the peas dry; even hurdles were used. Tripodding also stopped the peas from bleaching too much.

Mazagan beans were also occasionally grown; they were about half the size of Long Pods. When cut with a binder fairly early the pods did not split open and they were shocked with the butts upwards. I can remember a reaper (Hornsby) being used in around 1918 or 1919; that machine cut beans, and with rake-like sweeps swept the beans off the tray of the machine in wodges ready for hand tying and out of the way for the next cut.

Tares were also grown either for hay or for seed. All these crops left the land right for growing wheat. At the end of the First World War corn growing was profitable but in the early 1920s government support was withdrawn and prices, first of cereals and then of livestock, dropped. A lot of poorer ground went out of cultivation and in the late 1930s prices began to rise again. One thing the government did was to put a levy on imported wheat when the prices fell below the standard price paid to the farmers. On the stiffer parts of the Marsh and, particularly, on land that had been ploughed for generations, a lot of harrowing had to be done before drilling, often starting off with a four-horse harrow and gradually working the soil down finally with a pair of York harrows. These consisted of two 4 ft harrows hinged together and pulled by a pair of horses, with the harrows at an angle that stopped the harrow lines from following in the same lines. With these harrows the horseman followed, driving the horses with long rope reins; the man could if necessary lift the back of the harrows to let rubbish clear. A pair of lead horses pulled a 'Tett' or brush drill, and the drillman had to steer the drill from the side already drilled, that is, the front wheel of the drill had to be set to follow up the last drill furrow. The drill had to be carried round at the end. Drilling was usually started by marking three or four drill widths at each end of the field; this showed where the drill should start and stop at each end. With a Tett drill, changing the driving cogs was regulated by tipping the drill box backwards or forwards. Wheat was sown at the rate of 2½ to 3 bushels to the acre, barley 3 to 3½, and oats 4. Wheat was usually dressed with copper sulphate-bluestone before drilling, as a smut preventative. About 6 acres was a normal day's drilling and the drill was followed by the York harrows. When weather conditions permitted the corn was rolled and harrowed and also horse hoed in the spring. The horse hoe was set to match the drill rows, one boy leading the horse and a good man steering the hoe by handles at the back. After 1914 the practice of hand-hoeing cereals dwindled and by the mid 1920s it could not be afforded.

The start of the harvest varied from year to year according to the weather. Red clover (with Italian rye grass) was the first crop to be cut, followed by lucerne, turnip seed and swede seed. Winter barley was the first cereal followed by winter oats, then winter wheat, spring oats, spring wheat and finally spring barley, with the beans fitting in between and probably Tic beans last.

Bindering was started before the crop was fully ripe, but by the time the last field was done, some of the grain would be shedding.

It was hard going for the horses; if it was a heavy crop or if the land was wet two horses would be harnessed, one on each side of a pole, and another would go in front, led or ridden by a boy. The pair was driven by the horseman who had a long whip stuck up in a socket. From his seat, he could easily reach the three levers which controlled the work. One lever was to tilt the machine so that the cutter bar was raised or lowered, and the other two moved the sweeps backwards or forward, and raised them up or down, according to the height of the crop or which direction it was leading. There was also one more lever, which altered the position of the string on the sheaf. When a crop was leaning badly or was flat, a good third person with a stiff 8 ft pole was needed to try and keep the cut corn from lodging in a lump and to make it go up between the canvases past the packers into the tying (knotter) position, and then to throw the sheaf out. The man on the binder seat had to keep his eyes on the whole machine. It did sometimes happen that a whole row of sheaves came out untied. If there was a jam in the machine the horses automatically stopped when they felt a heavier load suddenly come onto their shoulders. The knotter was the trickiest part of the binder. Bindering about 6 or 7 acres would be a normal day's work.

Unless it was a very dry time all the corn was shocked after cutting; with beans there would be four sheaves to a shock, and the rest would be in tens or twelves. The shockers worked in twos, picking up the sheaves just above the point of balance in pairs, and jamming them to the ground so that there was at least a gap of 1 ft between the butts of the sheaves, and then pressing the tops tightly together. In a heavy crop there would only be about a sheaf's length between the rows thrown out by the binder. It helped when the time came to carry the corn if the shocks were even in size and the rows regular. When it was possible to manage without shocking, the sheaves would have to be turned with a fork before carrying. Three rows of sheaves would be turned one way, and the next three the opposite way and so on; that left a clear gap between each six rows for the wagons to go along.

When it came to the time to carry the corn, there would be two pitchers, one on each side of the wagon, and two boys to lead. The pitcher could help the loader by placing the sheaf carefully on the wagon and if the pitcher just drew his fork outwards there was no danger in the fork going into the loader's hand. At the front and rear of the wagon there were two standards, poles standing 6 ft above the wagon sides; the sheaves were tightly placed against these. After the outside sheaves had been laid, more sheaves were then placed in the middle to bind the outside ones on. A loader always had to keep the middle of the load full. Successive layers of sheaves were built up till it became difficult for the pitchers, and then an extra lot was put in the middle. A very windy day made life difficult for the loaders; either the sheaves blew up from where they were placed or perhaps the sheaf blew right off the wagon. But what was worse were thistly sheaves, sometimes they were so bad that a fork had to be used; gloves were some help but the thistles usually got inside.

Corn was stacked, if possible in a stack yard, with the right gap between one stack and the next, so that a thresher could just reach each stack. Before a stack was built a thick layer of straw was put on the ground to keep the sheaves from the damp earth; occasionally faggots were used. In the Marsh most stacks had a 22 ft diameter at the base which spread to 30 ft at the eaves; the stack was always started in the middle with a round shock, with each successive round of sheaves lying so that the ears of corn were resting on the previous round. After the first round, each successive layer of sheaves started on the outside of the stack – two sheaves thick with plenty of rounds lying on them to keep the middle of the stack higher than the outside.

If the crop had to be taken far, three wagons were ideal. One was loaded in the field, one was used for unloading and the third either going out or being brought back in. Four horses were best, one horse in the shafts of each wagon and the fourth horse in chain harness to help pull each load in. At the stack, one man was required on the load to pitch the sheaves on to the stack. The stacker laid all the outside sheaves; two people forked the sheaves across to the stacker who used his hands and knees to fit the sheaves in neatly. It was the last forker's job to place each sheaf the right way round for the stacker; a good team could make everyone's job easier. When it came to the roof of the stack the middle was made extra full so that all the sheaves were sloped downwards to let any rain run off. In the roof a hole was left for the first man on the stack to stand in; it was called The Lubbers Hole and he had to stand there till the stack was finished. Then the stacker would stand on a ladder to fill this hole up. Sometimes an elevator powered by a horse going round and round driving a horse gear was used; that at least saved one man and made work easier. If more horses, wagons and men were available, they were fitted in by doubling up some of the jobs, or perhaps they would start another stack. Alternatively if there were too few for team working, all the wagons would be loaded and then unloaded. An average stack took 6 or 7 acres of corn and provided a day's threshing; this yielded about sixty sacks. Thirty quarters (4½ cwt per quarter) equalled 6½ tons of wheat. Ten tons of straw was left. In the Marsh we grew too much straw in comparison with the yield of wheat. Most threshing was done by contractors called Clark Bros. of Bilsington. They had at least three threshing sets, and provided the engine driver and the feeder on the thresher, and several casual workers usually followed the thresher from farm to farm. Other than the driver and feeder, the most important man was the bond cutter. He controlled the flow of sheaves. There were three men on the corn stack and again each was to throw the sheaf so it was easier for the next man; two more were needed to look after the sacks and weigh and load them into a wagon, and four men were required behind the thresher tying the straw with a straw band in 28 lb trusses (two armfuls) – one man to pitch the trusses and two to stack it with an extra hand for the roof. Two boys were needed to rake out the chaff and cavings, and either carry it to a shed or load it onto wagons with hurdles round it.

Someone was also required to supply coal and water to the engine and this was usually a boy.

Unless the stacks were going to be threshed immediately after harvest, they had to be thatched with reed cut from suitable ditches at 1½d for a 3 ft circumference bundle. Thatching was often done piecework at so much a square of 10 ft × 10 ft.

Peas and beans would be the first to be thatched as they would be most vulnerable to rain. If a stack being built had to be covered up with a cloth, a turnip seed 12 ft × 12 ft cloth would be used or more likely slightly smaller at 10 ft × 12 ft. If that was well folded and roped a man would carry it up a ladder (2 cwt), but if it was at all wet it would have to be tied down with a wagon rope tied tight round the bottom of the stack.

Much pasture land was ploughed up during the First World War and afterwards farmers began to lay fields down to pasture. The value of Kent Perennial rye grass and Wild White Clover became recognized causing Wild White Clover to go up to 21s (£1.05) a pound.

Harold J. Body having bought Jesson Farm and laid it in, had a good show of Wild White Clover. He sold it in bloom for £750. I am certain that the buyer lost on it. In those days we did not know enough about the art of growing it. William Body of Tenterden put Wild White Clover in the public eye in about 1894 when he sent a grass seed mixture to some seed trials in Cheshire. His grass mixture probably contained perennial rye grass and meadow fescue as well as the Wild White Clover. As a result of the demand for Wild White Clover, Ransoms developed a clover huller which had two threshing drums, the second one to rub much of the seed from the clover heads. Hulling was a slow job as the clover was fed in by handfuls. When a field was to be laid down to clover, lucerne or pasture, the seeds would be sown with a seed barrow, which is a small drill, like a wheelbarrow, with a long box into which the seed was placed. In the box were brushes which were turned by a shaft attached to the wheels. Opposite each brush there was a revolvable brass disc which had one large ½ in hole and a series of small holes of about ⅛ in diameter. This was arranged so that seeds to be sown could be brushed out of either one or six small holes or the large hole or part thereof. The seeds were always sown in a crop of growing corn and a light one-horse harrow would be used to cover the seeds. The plant tare (a weed) varied according to the weather and occasionally grew so strong that extra care had to be used at harvest time to get the green growth dry. Spring barley was often the most difficult crop.

Very little meadow hay was made on the Marsh; in fact there was a financial penalty in most letting agreements for mowing permanent pasture and a much stiffer one for ploughing it. Also most tenancy agreements stated that there must be a certain acreage of land suitable and prepared for growing wheat, i.e. fallow, or land on which peas or beans had been growing. No straw or hay was to be sold off unless an equivalent value of manure was replacing it. All farms had cattle yards which had to be emptied and carted between April and harvest. The manure was either put straight on the land or carted to a maxen (a repository for manure) from which it would be carted and spread before ploughing. A good cart load would be dropped in five lumps, 15 ft apart and across a field, with the next row 15 ft from the last. Carting was often a wet-day job when the land was not fit for anything else. Other wet or spare-time jobs were bond making with oat straw or mending sacks with a large needle, and Fillis, the horseman, mended the harnesses and greased all the cart and wagon wheels and the wagon locks.

Horses were taken to the forge on wet days. This was at New Romney but sometimes Newchurch. Another job was fetching beach sand and pebbles from the New Romney Corporation hole, nearly opposite the Warren Inn; it was 6d a one-horse load or 1s for a two-horse wagon load. This was used for maintaining the farm road and stack yard.

In the 1920s the concrete wall from Haffenden to Buckhurst Cottages was built. Trib Boulding, who was the foreman of

Blacklock's steam ploughing gang during the summer and autumn and worked at Haffenden the rest of the year, built this wall with various mates. It is still standing sixty years on. Trib was a craftsman at whatever he turned his hand to: putting a new shaft onto a cart wheel, hanging a gate so that it swung properly, decarbonizing a Ford car and grinding the valves in, or making a cold chisel out of a ½ in spiral spring. He pulled down the Romney Windmill and laid out the timber for the sale.

A few acres of Wurtzel was grown for feeding cattle, sheep and pigs. The crop was clamped as near the point of use as possible, sometimes in a part of the barn adjoining the cattle yard. For young stock it was cut up and mixed with their corn.

About 240 ewes were kept at Haffenden and the surrounding lots of land. One lamb per ewe was all that was expected. There was not a regular flock but lambs were bought and sold according to the trade in the hopes of making a profit.

Romney Fair was always a busy day. Sheep, of course, were walked to or from there. Ham Street had a fair where improvers were bought as at the Tenterden September Fair. The Tenterden first Monday in May was one of the important fairs. There were about five different auctioneers, some selling at the same time according to the sheep trade. Those lambs to be sold walked as far as the Gibbet overnight, and any bought went straight back to the Gibbet to be fetched next day. It was quite a job to mother the ewes and lambs up. Biddenden Fair was held early in November where sheep and cattle were bought and sold. During the 1921/4 period Harold and John Hooker went into partnership with a Fowler steam ploughing tackle and threshing set.

Harold had, from his Romney Mill days, a certain amount of interest in the hay and corn trade. After leaving the Army in 1917, he was selling hay and straw to London merchants. If any farmer had surplus rushy grass, he was able to have it and make it into cheap hay for the London market. Similarly he bought truck loads of white African maize and sold them to several buyers, also trucks of condemned dates, which were fed to pigs and sheep, and some of the men were often seen leaving the store shed with sticky faces.

This led to Harold specializing in parcels of imported wheat – a deposit had to be paid on each lot. If the price for which he could sell the wheat went down, he still had to pay the full purchase price. It was a period of world depression and he finally had to give up as he was losing money – at one time £1,000 a day. With the outbreak of the Second World War in 1939 R.S. Body was called up and Harold, finding that he could not cope on his own, pulled all the strings he possibly could to get him released. He succeeded at the end of January 1940. War-time conditions and the emphasis on ploughing up pasture made it imperative to reduce the area of activities. In 1943 R.S. Body took over Vinal Farm which consisted of about 260 acres. This left Harold with Hope Farm, Fox Land, Mock Mill, Mantel Lane, Cuckoo, Dowels, and High House. He gradually reduced this but later bought Chapel Bank, which he disposed of after a year or two.

CHAPTER NINE

LANCASHIRE CATTLE MEN

Mr Robert Smith tells the story of how his family developed their business of cattle farming and dealing from the 1880s to the 1940s. He tells lively stories of cattle droving and daily life.

Our family's first involvement in the farming industry occurred during my great grandfather's lifetime. My grandfather, James Robert, was born into farming and purchased our present farm at about the time of his marriage in 1888. This is Thorp Farm about half a mile from the town of Royton.

A number of small industrial towns in Lancashire grew with the advent of the cotton industry. Around these centres the land was divided into what can best be described as 'family farms', some owned by the occupiers and the rest tenanted. These units were mostly worked by the family members alone, and their purpose was to provide the necessary foodstuff requirements for the growing industrial population.

This area, not being suitable for arable farming and with only a limited amount of vegetables being grown, was concentrated on livestock products. Milk was the main source of income for these farms and a concentrated dairy industry grew. Butter, cheese, eggs, poultry, pork and the end product of beef were all ancillary to the production of milk. The sale of this produce was made on a daily 'milk round' by horse and float from each individual farm. This daily routine would take four or five hours to complete and was made every single day. Christmas and Easter were holidays that other people experienced and did not affect the farming community. The horses employed on these rounds would in time get to know every customer, especially the ones who provided a crust of bread. They did not need to be led or driven, a shouted command from 150 ft or so away was sufficient to move them on to the next stopping place.

The very earliest information that I have of James Robert is a wonderful old tale about his marriage to my grandmother, Mary. I understand that the wedding had been arranged to take place at the Bethany Chapel, Goldhurst. At the time arranged for the ceremony, the registrar failed to attend and the wedding had to be postponed until the following morning. At this time both the bride and groom were engaged with their respective milk rounds, so at a specified time they met at the Chapel, tied their horses to convenient railings, and then went in to complete the wedding ceremony.

When James Robert had established his farming business at Thorp, he next turned his ambitions to cattle dealing. Dairy cattle must calve before they produce any milk. This production, after the initial flush, gradually diminishes over a period of months until it stops completely. Husbandry should now ensure that the cow calves again and once more starts to produce milk. However, for many reasons, cattle fall out of this cycle and are disposed of for beef. James Robert was surrounded by scores of milk-producing units giving him a ready market for supplying newly calved cattle on his doorstep. The problem in those days must have been supply. There was a market in the Milnrow area but it was a very limited affair. He was persuaded to go to Ireland for his stock. He made the return journey weekly by train and boat, while the cattle he bought returned by boat and train to Oldham, from where they would walk to Thorp. The carriage charge from Ireland to Oldham was 2s 6d (12½p) per head, and the value of a newly calved cow at that time was in the region of £12–£15.

In Ireland he would have been taken to the market and must have spent his first half hour or so alone, inspecting the cattle. On one occasion the vendor of one animal started a conversation attempting to sell the cow to him. The price asked was, say £14. The person who had taken James Robert to the market approached them at this point and saw that a deal was about to take place. He suggested that whatever difference in valuation there was between them, be divided. 'Ah!' said the vendor, 'but he has not bid anything yet.' 'Never mind that', said our friend. 'It's his first time in Ireland, so just divide it', whereupon the vendor did just that and the cow was purchased for £7.

Bartering and ringcraft was brought to a fine art by the cattle dealers in bygone years. It became a part of life for grandfather, father and myself. Based on confidence in the man that you traded with, relationships that have lasted for generations have formed. It was from these beginnings of a weekly intake of Irish cattle, that this part of the family business continued for the rest of James Robert's life.

When the cattle arrived at Thorp, farmers in our area who were in need of a replacement milk cow would come to the farm and purchase one or two. It must be remembered that at this time transport was limited primarily to the horse, although longer journeys were made by train. This meant that the majority of farmers who were tied to the daily routine of producing and selling their milk were unable to travel any distance for their replacement needs. The purchase of these cattle at Thorp by individual farmers meant that, because of this purchase of new cattle they had their own dry cattle to dispose of, so a two-way trade developed.

This in itself had two or three related effects. First the cattle had to be moved from Thorp to whichever farm they were destined. How was this done? They walked them, of course. This was mostly done by casual labour drawn from the cotton mills. Their payment was a tip from the purchaser, and the amount could be 3d (1p), 6d (2½p) or 1s (5p), depending on the giver. Journeys could be anything up to 5 or 6 miles each way, but circumstances in the cotton industry were such that there was always a group of young men waiting in the barn for the next cow to be sold, and with their fingers crossed so that when their turn came it would be a quiet cow and a generous tipper.

The second effect of the two-way trade was that suddenly there was a concentration of cattle at Thorp which had finished their milking lives and needed to be slaughtered. A butchering side to the business was started therefore and what is now the workshop of the farm was the first slaughterhouse used. The rails for hanging the carcases are still there today.

The third dimension of the two-way trade concerned the return to Thorp of dry cattle which were in calf but not due to calve for some time. Obviously these could not all be retained at Thorp for their numbers would grow beyond the capacity of the farm.

A new livestock industry must have been evolving at that time. Farms in the more remote parts of the country were changing their aims to the supply of the now needed milking cattle. This was particularly so in the Yorkshire Dales and the northern area of Lancashire, where a number of cattle markets were developing to accommodate this new trade. Preston, with its convenient railway link was the next venue for James Robert's supply of milking cattle. I have often heard that these cattle were transported by train from Preston to Rochdale and then walked the final 3 miles to Thorp. It must have been a very long day for both men and beasts.

Preston provided an outlet for the dry, in-calf cattle which were arriving at Thorp. These cattle would be taken to the market there and sold to the local farmers. Here, they would be kept until they calved again, whereupon they would be re-sold back into the milk-producing sector.

One memorable week, of which my own father never tired of relating, occurred when he was seventeen years old. At that time in 1917, in the depths of the First World War, the infant Railway Men's Union was flexing its muscle and called a strike. Farmers, however, have neither time nor sympathy for strikers, so, a day earlier than usual, James Robert and his son Hartley journeyed to Preston by horse and trap. They purchased their cattle there and then proceeded to walk them home. This homeward journey took two days, with an overnight stop in the Boston area, where the cattle were rested, fed and milked.

James Robert must have travelled ahead, according to the story, leaving the cattle with my father and his dog. On a journey as long as this, one cow would develop as the leader, and answering to the actions of the dog would lead the herd on the correct route. The roads were quiet and traffic-free in those days, and the journey was quite feasible, but my father always said what a welcome sight Royton Town Hall was as he came over the hill from Rochdale.

Another incident often recalled concerns a dog and Preston. One of the local farmers must have been in need of a working dog and grandfather happened to have one available. This dog was taken to Preston on the train, collected at the market by the new owner, and taken from there to his home. However, a few days later the dog arrived back at Thorp in a very travel-weary condition. Needless to say, he remained at Thorp for the rest of his life. How did it find its way back to Thorp from Preston?

There was no power supply to the farmhouse at Thorp. Lighting in both house and farm was by oil lamp. Coal fires were the only means of heating and cooking. In the living room of the farmhouse stood a very substantial fire range, always with a large iron kettle on the hob to give an immediate supply of hot water. A larger quantity of warm water was contained in a boiler built into one side of the range. This boiler had to be filled by hand; usually a couple of buckets at a time would be poured in. The heated water was also drawn out by hand by means of a ladling can which was dipped in and the contents poured into a waiting bucket. This water, more often than not, had a faint sooty smell, but it was always used for washing oneself and for all the normal household cleaning.

Built into the opposite side of the fire range was the oven, with its big heavy iron door. Here all the cooking was done. One day each week the fire was stoked particularly high. This was baking day when a full week's supply of bread, cakes, and pies would be made. The smell of newly baked muffins was something to be remembered.

In the kitchen, the length of one entire wall was taken up by a stone flag shelf built on brick supports to about 2 ft 6 in height. This complemented the hollowed out stone sink under the window. Next, into the corner was built a set boiler, a common enough piece of equipment in houses of that era. This set boiler can best be described as an elongated half sphere, made from cast iron, and bricked into its setting with a fireplace and flue. They were used for the weekly laundry sessions, providing very hot water in the Dolly Tubs with their 'possers' and on the rubbing boards with their blocks of carbolic soap. Quite often this carbolic soap was used to wash us when we were small children and it was woe betide anyone who suffered it in the eyes or nose!

Fresh water for drinking was carried daily to every house in Thorp. This was obtained from the spring around which the village was built. Water for general household use was pumped into the kitchen from a collection well and was just the natural rainfall draining from our fields. The pump, as I remember it, was a huge cast iron affair fixed into one end of the stone sink. Operated by a long curved handle, it produced a resounding gush of water followed by nothing until the next rush arrived. This pump represented progress because it provided the only running water to any of the houses in Thorp.

The cellar, built as an annexe to the kitchen, was supposed to be the cold room. It was used for the storage of foodstuffs and dairy products, especially in the summer to deter the flies. On its own flag shelf I have seen many a side of bacon, smothered in salt, in the process of being cured. Meat products were stored in a meat safe, a container made from gauze which provided ventilation while still keeping the flies out.

There are two things that I particularly remember about our grandmother. First was the weekly churning of butter. Fixed into the dairy floor was a hand-turned milk separator. Surplus milk was fed through this contraption and gearing would ensure that the inner components revolved at a fantastic speed. Skim milk would emerge from one of the two outlet tubes and was used for pig feeding; cream from the other was used for making the butter. How the machine performed this operation neither I, nor anyone else of my generation had any idea, but it certainly worked. A week's supply of cream was built up and stored in the cellar in an earthenware jar. For the last few hours before churning this was placed next to the fire hearth to bring the cream up to the required temperature. A thermometer mounted on a wooden float registered this. When ready it was transferred into the churn, a typical revolving barrel with an air vent and inspection window. The churning operation would take twenty minutes or so and was an arm-aching process which I experienced many, many times, but when grandmother salted the newly made butter in her wooden bowl, weighed out the required amounts and patted them into shape, all with intricate designs worked into them, it was magic for us children. The sample we tasted from the end of her finger was our reward.

The other most lasting memory that I have of grandmother is how she used to make the herb beer each year when haymaking time arrived. What a delicious drink it was.

As was to be expected, haymaking was a very labour intensive job in those days. It was usual to see fifteen or twenty people working in line across a field. These would be our casual staff from the cotton mills. Their pay was 6d (2½p) per hour for learners, who spent most of their time resting aching arms or nursing blistered hands. This went up to 10d (4p) an hour when they had acquired the necessary technique of handling rake or fork which enabled them to work continuously from early in the day, as soon as the dew had lifted, until after darkness had fallen.

On the Way to the Hayfield. From a painting by a unknown artist, originally published as a postcard about 1910.

dew had lifted, until after darkness had fallen.

I wonder why, that for every memory I have of a wet summer, there are many more memories of sunny hot ones when it used to be said, 'Throw your jacket under the hedge at the start of hay-time, and never pick it up again until hay-time is over'. However, these long hot sunny days led to large quantities of liquid refreshment being consumed and grandmother's herb beer was very welcome. It was made from local plants and yeast; she used to have gallons upon gallons of it fermenting in a row of earthenware bowls lined up on her kitchen stone shelf.

As children, our own involvement in this operation was the collection of the ingredients; these were mainly dandelion leaves for brewing, and then later we would deliver the finished product in gallon jars up to the hayfield. Needless to say, we always sampled our fair share of this marvellous brew. Since grandmother's death

Bringing in the straw, from a photographic postcard, 1910. (Author's collection)

other members of the family have tried to repeat her recipe for this beer but never with any success. The secret must sadly have died with her.

The most significant happening during James Robert's and Mary's later years was the supply of electricity to Thorp. This occurred about the year 1933, and one can imagine the impact that it had on everyone. No more filling, lighting or trimming a large assortment of lamps. Just the flick of a switch and any room in the house or farm buildings would be a hundred times lighter than ever before. Other benefits followed immediately: cookers with which the heat could be controlled and where water could be boiled without first having to light a fire in a morning. Radio brought music into homes which had known nothing but a piano, a phonograph or the headphones of a crystal set. The purchase of a vacuum cleaner was an event which involved the whole family. I demonstrated in the farmhouse with grandmother, mother and aunts in attendance.

Changes were also taking place in the cattle-dealing enterprise at about this time. The development of the motor vehicle continued and lorries for the transporation of livestock were evolving; these opened up a much wider area for the purchase of cattle. In fact, Hellifield in Yorkshire became the next place for this supply. It was found that cattle from this limestone area were much hardier and a more healthy type. In Hellifield there was also a large market for sheep which provided the necessary animals for the slaughtering business.

The first car to become part of the farm was ATF 14, a Rover Fourteen, purchased new in 1936 at a cost of £330. This car, with daily use on rough farm roads, gave an excellent service for some seventeen years until 1953. Another Rover, then an Austin, followed in quick succession but there was no quality built into these post Second World War cars. In 1957 we purchased our first Land Rover, and have owned one of these vehicles ever since.

This Rover was petrol driven and cost £750. The second, purchased in 1962, was also petrol driven and cost £900. In 1968 we changed to a diesel model, which was a more expensive purchase but more economical to run. The cost of this was £1,014. Our present car, also a diesel, which we have owned since 1975 cost £2,700. The price of a new one today (1995) is around £20,000.

James Robert never did learn to drive. He preferred to be driven by my father or cousin Fred, both of whom by this time had taken over all responsibility for the running of the farm and slaughterhouse. James Robert was active in his capacity of 'interested father' until his very last day. That day, 27 March 1936, is imprinted very clearly in my memory. He must have been having an off day, and I in turn was absent from school for some illness or other. Consequently, the pair of us were confined to the front room of the farmhouse for the afternoon, where on the radio we listened to the commentary of the launching of the *Queen Mary*, the first of the great Cunard liners. That evening James Robert suffered a heart attack and died immediately.

My father, Hartley's main interest throughout life was to buy and sell cattle. With a competent staff running the slaughterhouse, he was able to devote his time to the purchase of the stock required there, and also the buying and selling of the dairy cattle passing through the farm.

Irishmen came over seasonally for the haymaking, sleeping in the barn loft and were reported to be usually the worse for drink each night. Jokes were often played on them: one involved a white horse blanket which was pulled up to the barn roof by a rope passing over a beam. When the group of men were settling for the night, the rope was released and with a whirring noise the white blanket fluttered down out of the shadows onto them. One can imagine the consternation caused. I'll bet none of those Irishmen used the ladder to get down from the loft.

My own induction into the working of the farm began when I was about eight or nine years old. I was made responsible for the milking of one cow. This cow, quiet and easily drawn, was specially selected for me to learn to milk. I would milk it each morning before going to school and again in the evening when I returned. As I became more proficient I was given two, then three, until I was eventually able to take a full place in the milking team. Another of my early morning, pre-school, jobs was in summertime to bring the horses from the field into the stable ready for the milk round and the daily farm work. In wintertime, with any ice on the ground, I would take the horse for that day's milk round to the blacksmith's to have frost nails put into its shoes. These nails were just ordinary farriers nails for shoeing a horse, but with the nails protruding for about ½ in or so to give a grip on any ice that might be encountered. These nails were worn flat by one day's use and had to be replaced daily.

Over the years we owned many horses, mostly willing and of

good character, but even so we had one or two favourites. My very earliest memory, I must only have been about two years old at the time, was being carried by grandfather into the field to see Captain, a horse that he had owned for some twenty-six years or so which was a very great age for a horse. Big Billy was a retired hunter living at the slaughterhouse. His work was to pull a retail sale meat van round the district. Nellie was a dark chestnut, Irish-bred mare, very strong with a temper to match. I still have the mark on my wrist made by her teeth. Prince was the best of the lot and took old Captain's role when my father took my sons as babies into the field each Sunday to stroke Prince and sit them on Prince's back. Prince was with us when tractors took over from horses and he lived a retired life with us for many years. His only work was to pull a raking machine at haytime. After a full year without harness we could put him into the shafts of this machine and he would walk quietly on as if he had never stopped working.

At one time we owned a mare of a very unusual colour: it was a light roan, common enough in the shorthorn breed of cattle which abounded at the time, but very rare in a horse. Her name, Beauty, reflected her appearance. One summer's morning I went as usual to bring the horses from the field. During the night they had broken through the fence into our neighbour's land and Beauty had cut a back leg getting through the wire. It was not a big cut, more deep than long, but it still looked nasty and needed treatment from the vet. Within a few days lockjaw infection started and the horse became completely rigid in every part of her body. She stood in the loose box and could have been made from iron. There was nothing to do but to have her destroyed as quickly as possible.

I shall never forget the very first cow I bought on my own. This was at a farm sale where the farm was closing down and everything was being sold. The cow was newly calved, a blue shorthorn, and I thought then, and still do, that its price of £47 was cheap on the day. This cow was immediately re-sold after its arrival at Thorp. I was fourteen years old at the time.

I must have been about eleven years old when I started to work at the slaughterhouse, learning the trade. Every Sunday morning, after milking, there would be a drove of cattle from Thorp to the slaughterhouse in Royton. On arrival I had my own overalls and set of knives. The first jobs that I was entrusted with were to take the heads off each beast and the emptying of the stomachs. By lunchtime I had to finish, run home, clean up and attend Sunday school in the afternoon. This part of my training came to a very abrupt end when I was thirteen years old: one day I was hanging a cow's head on a hook, something I had done hundreds of times before, but I must have been standing on a bit of fat and my feet slipped backwards. I finished with my own head hanging through the chin on that hook. This happened in the spring of 1939; later that year the war broke out and all slaughtering came under government control with privately owned slaughterhouses having to close down. Some ten or twelve years later, when the restrictions were lifted, the area in which the slaughterhouse stood was scheduled for clearance and the business was never re-started.

The numbers of dairy cattle passing through the farm grew substantially during and just after the war years. With the rationing of imported concentrates cattle could not be fed to sustain their milk yields, so greater numbers were kept to supply the amount of milk needed by each farm. At the most busy time of the year during October to December, thirty or forty newly calved cattle would be brought from Hellifield on a Thursday, and would all have been sold by Friday night. On the Saturday my father would have to go to farms in the Airton Gurgrave area and buy another ten or twenty. The farm was a busy place with all the beet and in-calf cattle returning to Thorp. I once made a count of the number of cattle in one 14 acre field and there were 163 on that day.

The beef cattle had to be sent to Ministry Certification Centres throughout the war years. The nearest was in Rochdale but later moved to Mode Wheel on Salford Docks. Two, three or four wagon loads would go each Monday. When the move to Salford was made my father would travel with the cattle. He was very experienced and he was asked to join the staff at this centre; he became official grader for the Ministry, certifying the hundreds of cattle which were presented each Monday.

When I reached my seventeenth birthday I was able to hold a driving licence; from then on, every Monday, I would take the car with a trailer behind, visiting all the farms which had contacted us, and buy the calves which had been born that week, taking them to Salford. One hilarious episode happened during a week when the car was in need of some repair and I borrowed a rather old van from a neighbour. I remember that there were seventeen calves that day. While I was driving up a steep hill in Pendlebury, the van doors burst open and there were calves dashing around all over the road. It was lunchtime and a nearby workforce was coming out for their break, so there was plenty of help to round up my load.

The business continued through the war years. Farmers would come in their dozens when the weekly consignments of cattle arrived. Most of the cattle were still walked from Thorp to their destinations but some of the more progressive farmers were now having their stock delivered by wagon. For the others, the difference between a tip of 1s (5p) to a drover, and the price of 2s 6d (12½p) for a wagon still had to be considered. The driving we had down to a fine art. Single cows would be led on a rope, whether they wanted to or not. Most could be educated in a few minutes. The knack was to keep the animal side on to the holder of the rope so that it constantly pulled itself round in a circle. If ever it managed to face away from the holder of the rope there was no way of stopping it. If we had more than one cow we would just drive them loose. This kept us very fit and we would run for miles. From time to time there was the odd really rogue cow that we could do nothing with at all and a horse-drawn cattle float had to be used. This cart was designed primarily for the transport of pigs but could be called into use for these really wild cattle, or the odd cow casualty that could not walk. There were many incidents of cattle entering houses through a door being left open and what a shock that was for the people inside! Gravestones in cemeteries were kicked over and the odd cow jumped into the canal on the way to Middleton. One day, my brother had a cow jump into the lodge of the Balderstone Mill. When it had been dragged out, the engineer of the mill came out with his brew can and asked if he could have a drop of milk for his tea.

Our dog Jock was marvellous with cattle. On droving expeditions he knew every opening and gate, even parts of weak fencing that we had to pass, and he would be there in place before the cattle arrived. As often as not, all that we were needed for was to keep the cattle moving from behind. There was once an accident when he was just a young dog involving the mowing machine. I was mowing with two horses when the knife became blocked with old grass which happened quite often. I stopped the horses to clear the blockage and Jock came over to me; one of the horses moved position, the knife flicked up and Jock had two pads cut from a front paw. The following day, with his leg smothered in bandages he still insisted on working with the cattle. We had to shut him indoors until he recovered – he was so keen and willing to work.

Little did we realize that changes were occurring which would completely end the structure of farming as we knew it. People were demanding better living accommodation. It became the fashion for every local council to demolish large areas of older property and build new houses for the displaced occupants. Many buildings of unbelievable character were lost at this time. Of course more land was needed for this property and this was to devastate the farming world as we knew it. The farms of families to whom we had sold cattle started to disappear, not in ones or two, but in dozens, in every part of the area that our trade covered. Wherever one looked, bricks and cement were replacing grass. In the Kingsway area of Rochdale there were once many farms where now lies a housing estate. More than twenty farms have gone on the eastern side of the road from Oldham to Ashton. In Middleton is the huge Langley

Estate which was once farmland and in Alkrington, among twelve others, five separate farms, each belonging to a member of the Wolstenholme family, have been completely obliterated. Great areas of agricultural land were being lost as a result of housing and industrial development. One does not need a strong imagination to realize what this did to our cattle dealing trade.

A few of the families who were dispossessed owned their land and received some compensation while others were compensated for loss of livelihood. By this time very few sons were following their fathers into a farming life. They were able to compare it with other occupations and refused to accept the conditions imposed by a life on the land with cattle. Consequently, many of these families ended their association with farming at this point. Even on our own farm, one of our employees walked home one afternoon leaving a horse in the shafts of a cart and the cart half-filled with manure. He had had enough and within the week he was working on a building site.

Luckily mechanization was fast filling the gap caused by the lack of manpower. Machines for milking the cattle were introduced. Tractors replaced the horses and were powering increasingly sophisticated machines. Four or five of our old hands still turned up each year at haymaking time, but this was more for the pleasure of practising old skills, and the renewing of friendships than any financial consideration. Over the years though, they have slowly one by one died off.

CHAPTER TEN

A YORKSHIRE FARMER'S SON

Mr John Norris of Driffield, Yorkshire, remembers life on his father's farm in the early years of the twentieth century. He describes farming methods in that area.

In 1913 my father rented a 200 acre farm. I was nearly seven at the time. I can remember the men working from 6 a.m. until 6 p.m. Mondays to Fridays, and to 5 p.m. on Saturdays with one hour off for their midday meal. Labourers' wages were about 15*s* (75p) per week. Single men and youths normally lived-in and were hired for the year which included a fixed sum plus board and lodgings.

They attended to the horses and cows. This meant that horsemen got up at about 4.45 a.m. to groom and feed the horses. They went to breakfast around 5.40 a.m. By then the horses would be geared and ready for work at 6 a.m. The foreman would have been around the stables before breakfast arranging the work for the day. The cowmen would be milking at this time. The farmer's wife and her maid would be responsible for feeding those who lived-in. On a farm this size there would probably be two or three living in, as well as the maid. On farms of more than 300 acres probably a hind [a skilled farm-worker] would be responsible for boarding those 'living in'. He was also the foreman and in many cases, did most of the daily running of the farm. The farmer would discuss with him the night before the work he wanted done on the morrow. The hind's wife saw to the feeding of the men and on some of the larger farms there could be six or seven men to be fed and housed. The farmer had to provide bedsteads, bedding, crockery, tables and forms plus a supply of milk for the hind house. He then paid the hind a fixed rate per week for the men housed.

The hours worked per week were reduced before 1920 with no work on Saturday afternoon; March to October the men worked from 7 a.m. until 5.30 p.m. and for the remainder of the year 7 a.m. until 5 p.m. Wages in 1922 for a labourer were £1 10s per week (£1.50). Horsemen were paid according to status; for instance, wagoners who carried corn and 'lived in' were paid from £35 to over £40 for the year; the third lad who carried corn £30 to £35, while the third lad who did not carry corn up to £30; and young lads from the first 'year off' between £15 and £25. They were expected to work two hours each day attending to the horses and three hours at weekends.

A wagoner was expected to carry sacks of corn up steps, some weighing up to 20 stones – wheat was weighed in 18 stone sacks, barley in 16 stone sacks and oats in 12 stone sacks. I believe beans were weighed at 19 stone per sack. Corn was sold by the quarter from the Measure Table of 4 gills being 1 pint, and 2 pints equalling 1 quart etc. The average weight of a bushel of wheat was 4½ stones, of barley 4 stones and oats 3 stones.

A typical breakfast menu for farm workers in those days was cold beef, dry bread and pie (apple, jam, fig or rhubarb) according to the time of the year, with tea to drink. Dinner varied during the week. At our house we had the same menu as the farm workers and the joint was taken from our table to the men's. Monday would be cold roast beef with vegetables followed by milk pudding; on Tuesday and Friday we had hot beef pie with vegetables, and hot fruit pie; on Wednesday it was broth, suet dumplings, boiled beef and vegetables. Broth was made from boiled beef and bacon and sometimes ham, with some vegetables such as potatoes, cabbage, turnip, carrots, peas and parsnips. The bacon and ham were home cured as we usually killed four pigs each year. This was perhaps a heavy diet but work began at 7 a.m. and went on till 12 noon, with no break for drinks, then from 1 p.m. to 5.30 p.m. again with no break. Tea was boiled bacon, dry bread and pie washed down by tea.

During haytime and harvest there were drinks with a snack at around 9.30 to 9.45 a.m. and 3.30 to 3.45 p.m., as work then went on until 7 or 8 p.m. There were also drinks and a snack on threshing days. At one time farm men had boiled milk for breakfast and tea. On our farm they had tea in the morning and also milk boiled in the side oven. This went on until about 1920.

I cannot remember the prices of corn at that time but it was sold by the quarter (2 stones) and not by the ton. Of course, during the First World War I was still at school but I know that the prices rose sharply; corn and stock for instance sold from the farm, together with cake meal, repairs and implements which had to be bought in all went up. But prices began to fall after the war. We moved farm again in 1922 and 1929. The price of wheat in 1929 was £2 per quarter but it began to fall after that date. The wheat quota payment was introduced in the 1930s and barley, that is good malting barley, was £1 0s 6d (£1.02½) per quarter. Wages at that time had gone up to £1 15s (£1.75).

If men were living in between 1932 and 1934 the farmer could deduct 15s (75p) per week for board and lodging. The wages of a wagoner had been done away with and when a man reached twenty-one he had to be paid at least 35s (£1.75) irrespective of his ability. Those under twenty-one were paid according to their age.

Threshing was done by engaging a man who had the tackle. He would come into the stack yard the day before, probably from a neighbouring farm and set the machine, engine and elevator or baler to the stack to be threshed; before leaving for home he and his helper would have a meal. Then next morning he would be at the farm before 6 a.m. to get steam up. He and his helper would get their meals at the farm until they left for the next farm. The price for threshing in the 1920s was about £3 10s (£3.50) per day, which included the wages of the helper. The helper usually 'fed' the machine. Extra helpers were paid 7s (35p) per day at this time, and if engaged to carry corn 1s (5p) per day extra. If you were strong enough to carry it, it was considered one of the best jobs of a threshing day. The farmer was responsible for providing coal for the engine and a supply of water; the coal tender of the engine also had to be filled up for the journey to the next farm.

Work on the farm at this time was mainly hand labour and consisted of: ploughing, with a team of horses (two to a single-furrow plough), harrowing with two, three or four horses, drilling with two horses, bindering with three or four horses, grass reaping with two horses, scriffling with one, horse-raking with one, and leading with wagons two horses (during harvest). Some corn was still mown with scythes from 1913 to 1930.

Other jobs were hoeing turnips, stooking corn, turning hay with rakes, and pulling turnips for stock and sheep. On the majority of farms at this time turnips and mangolds were cut by hand-turned cutters. When used for cutting up the turnips and mangolds for the sheep, the cutter would be in the field and the sheep in folds. Turnips were carried in scuttles to the stock in the foldyards, and in many cases, straw was carried by the forkful and there was quite an art in making a good forkful. Hay was cut out of the stack with a special knife.

Water for the stock in the foldyard had to be pumped into troughs; this was done by the herdsman, although the horsemen generally took a turn on a Sunday. In summer, the supply of water for the stock in the fields had to be supplied by water cart and this was a job that was done seven days a week. On three of the farms my father farmed, we had streams running through our land so the stock had a running water supply. On most farms nowadays there is a mains supply.

All my farming life I have been on a tenanted farm. My first farm was with my father who took me into partnership (with the agreement of the landlord) and later with my brother-in-law. An agreement was drawn up and signed by the landlord or his agent and

124

Sharpening the scythe, late 1930s. This was considered a skilled job. The worker demonstrating this task is wearing a smock which would have been the standard worker's dress in his grandfather's day. (Mr Simmonds)

agreement was drawn up and signed by the landlord or his agent and the tenant. There were certain conditions the landlord had to fulfil, such as keeping the farmhouse and buildings in good condition – making sure it was waterproof and structurally maintained; some provided paint but the occupier had to do the painting. The tenant was expected to follow the normal rotation of crops with no more than two corn crops together and turnips and clover seeds to be grazed by sheep. All hedges had to be slashed every two years and boundary hedges every year. No straw was to be sold off the farm but had to be turned into manure and used on the land.

Some had an agreement for providing men, horses and carts to convey coals from the station to the landlord's residence. The number of teams of men and horses varied according to the rent you paid. In fact, the agreement was drawn up in accordance with the farming

Cutting corn, from a postcard of about 1910. The team of mowers are using scythes.
(Author's collection)

practice of that area which also varied from one estate to another and was considered to be good husbandry at that time. Several of these kinds of agreements existed until the 1960s and '70s. Nowadays, things have changed so much: most of the corn is drilled in the autumn, whereas years ago the main drilling was done in the spring. The four and five years' rotation was common practice until the Second World War. Four year rotation was wheat, turnips, barley or oats, followed by clover seeds for grazing sheep. Five year rotation was wheat, barley or oats, turnips, barley or oats, and clover seeds.

The main fertilizers used were Kainite Superphosphate, sulphate of ammonia, basic slag and lime. Now fertilizers are compounds specially made for different crops. In the old East Riding of Yorkshire there were about four different types of farming: on strong or heavy clay, carr land (which was peaty), wold land and

CHAPTER ELEVEN

DAIRY FARMING IN SOMERSET

Mr Douglas W. David was the son of a dairy farmer. He describes the work he did on the farm as a boy and the work of the cowmen. He later worked on a number of farms and goes on to describe changes that have taken place in the industry.

My father was a dairy farmer in East Somerset. One of my earlier recollections is the news of the Wall Street Crash in 1929 when I was twelve years old. The recession that followed grew worse as the 1930s wore on.

The farm was 270 acres and we employed a cowman, who lived in the tied cottage adjoining the farmhouse, and a teenaged lad. My two brothers and I were also fully employed out of school hours. The cowman's cottage was stone-built, three-bedroomed, with flagstone floors at ground level, a living room with an open-range cooker, a scullery with a brick-built copper for laundry work, and a small larder. There was a cold water tap outside the back door and an earth-closet in the vegetable garden.

Frank Fowler, the cowman, was paid 32s per week (£1.60) in 1930 with overtime at 9d (3½p) an hour rising to 1s (5p) in about 1932. This overtime was only paid for work done after teatime in the summer months but work such as haymaking or harvesting corn, casual emergencies such as difficult calvings, colic in one of the cart-horses in the middle of the night, or the rounding-up of escapees on Sundays, was all attended to free. I don't recall what the lad's pay was but imagine it was between £1 and 25s (£1.25) a week.

Frank had three young children as well as his wife and himself to feed and clothe on this very low wage. He had no rent, of course, and had a pint or so of free milk per day, with firewood from the adjoining Cogley Wood for the taking, and he was allowed potatoes and swedes from the arable fields. Rabbits were very plentiful in those days, but were seldom eaten in the warmer months. We made several hogsheads of cider in the autumn and this was available to all and sundry who cared to brave the cobwebs in the cellar. Frank's elder son had some moletraps; the skins of his victims were scraped, nailed to a board to dry, and collected for cash by the man who delivered paraffin and bloaters to the village.

The day's work started with milking by hand the sixty or so dairy Shorthorns. All hands took part, including the boss himself; it was a chore that had to be done morning and evening, seven days a week, summer and winter. It was a quiet operation as a rule, every man on his three-legged stool and heavy-tinned pail with rigid handle gripped between the knees, the younger members discussing the sporting fixtures or singing the latest Bing Crosby hit, while father and Frank would be involved with higher things such as the weather and crop prospects. The evening milking signalled the end of the working day – except in summer, of course – and all would be home shortly after 6 p.m.

The week ended officially at 1 p.m. on Saturday but as the cows would be brought in for the evening milking at 3 p.m. it was little different from any other weekday. Sunday was a day of rest for the shire horses but for the rest of us it was two milking sessions and the feeding of pigs and poultry and the like.

Most Saturday evenings Frank's friend from a neighbouring farm would call on him; they would wet their whistles from the cider-barrel and then walk across the fields the mile or so to the village pub where they would enjoy the Shepton Mallet Brewery's ale, retailing at 4d or 5d (2p) a pint. The two served together in the Somerset Light Infantry in France and Mesopotamia during the First World War; both were very popular in the locality and there was usually a farmer or two in the bar only too willing to top up their mugs. Without this and the cider I doubt that they could have afforded many drinks on their pay. Sunday mornings would see a return trip for a 'hair of the dog' to cure the effects of the previous evening and most of the village men over sixteen years or so would join them. It was always referred to as 'going to Church'. The local police never bothered the landlord so age limits were little problem – I well remember my young brother and myself getting drunk at the age of fifteen and sixteen respectively.

There was no clock-watching in those days – none of us owned a watch but we seemed to develop a sense of time and when the wind was in the right direction, the clocks would be checked against the whistle of the Cornish Riviera Express as it hurtled through Bruton Station at 12.30 p.m. on the dot. When working in the fields adjoining the road it was customary to hail passers-by for a time-check. One elderly villager who was a regular foot passenger on the highway, would invariably shout back the single word 'Twenty'! Whether it was 'twenty to' or 'twenty past' was anybody's guess. It was assumed that either the watch he drew from his waistcoat pocket was not a working model or he had yet to master the art of reading it!

None of the yards around the buildings had been concreted in the 1930s and mud was a big problem in the winter months. I don't know whether rubber-boots were on the market then but I don't remember the menfolk wearing anything other than heavy hob-nailed boots with leather leggings, ex-Army puttees or string tied under the knee to hoist trouser bottoms above the worst of the mud. Periodically the mud would be swept into heaps and carted back to the meadows whence it came; the only problem with this method was that all the loose stones were swept up with it and these had to be picked up by hand and returned to the yards to avoid damage to the mowing-machines when the haymaking season started. This was a task for the youngest members of the labour force and the older men facetiously referred to it as 'diamond-picking'.

Poor Frank Fowler died from a gastric disease before reaching retirement age; some were of the opinion that a lifetime on a diet that included so much acid cider had not helped matters. Everyone who knew him grieved at his loss, always cheerful and kind-hearted especially to us when we were boys. He had known nothing but hard work and penury all his life for, to the best of my knowledge, he never had a proper holiday away from the farm. His widow is still living and fending for herself in an old people's bungalow. She is well over ninety years of age. Their three children are still alive but sadly the daughter and youngest son both suffer from multiple sclerosis. I sometimes wonder whether their diet in their early years was too simple and basic and lacking some of the vital elements needed to ensure good health.

In 1932 the manager of the local Labour Exchange asked the neighbourhood farmers if they could help with seasonal work for the unemployed in Bruton. Father was agreeable and one sunny morning three men presented themselves at the farmhouse, having walked up from the town. They were put to helping us haul the hay that was fit; at 1 p.m. we stopped for dinner and at 2 p.m. they failed to re-appear and we never saw them again.

About this time a young man knocked on the door, having cycled all the way from Westbury in Wiltshire searching for work. He said he had no experience of farm work but was desperate for anything as he had a young family to support. Farmers as well as their workers were now feeling the pinch and father said he was unable to help, but as we were just stopping for lunch he was welcome to join us in our staple diet of bread and cheese and tea. At this the poor chap broke down and wept, saying he had had

At this the poor chap broke down and wept, saying he had had nothing to eat since the previous day. I'm sure we were all moved by this but I guess he felt better after some food and a cigarette, and a couple of tins of something from the larder for his family.

The owner of the corn mill in Bruton took the trouble to tell all his farmer customers to be careful not to deprive their stock of feedstuff when trying to cut down on expenses as that would solve nothing. He would continue to supply them and said we could worry about paying the bills when times improved. None forgot this magnanimous gesture and the firm thrives to this day.

In 1949 I took a post as herdsman on a farm in Dorset. The term cowman had gone out of fashion and you became either herdsman or dairyman. The title carter for the man responsible for

A farmer with his prize bull, 1920s. (Author's collection)

wage had been fixed at £4 10s (£4.50) so that most of my ilk were paid between £6 and £7 a week to cover weekend work and added responsibility. A rent-free house and unlimited milk went with the post. Eventually I returned to Somerset to manage a herd of eighty-five pedigree Friesians, with occasional help from one of the other hands.

It was a far cry from the days of my youth when everyone had a hand in every task on the farm. Now my days were fully taken up with calf registration, tattooing numbers in ears, telephoning the Artificial Insemination Centre, national milk recording, cleaning and maintaining machinery, preparing cattle for sale or showing, on top of the twice daily milking and calf delivery when required. All this meant that no longer would I join the others in hoeing, ploughing or harvesting, to enjoy the gossip and banter; I had to learn to talk to myself and the animals – the milking machine was far too noisy to be able to converse with my helper.

Once experienced in the work there was no difficulty in getting a post but for some reason no one stayed long with the same employer. In my own case, I found myself getting restless about every five years, ostensibly for an extra pound in the wage-packet, but in fact, probably more out of boredom and the pressure to do more and more in the same number of hours. I also found it quite a strain to be responsible for so many expensive animals. By the time I reached middle age it was becoming too physically demanding and I gave up to take a post in a business, serving farmers.

I have seen many changes in the last fifty years but I have difficulty in finding much in the way of true progress. It is true that workers on the land are better fed and clothed, have decent holidays and can afford a car, but on the debit side mechanization has caused such an exodus from rural villages into towns that village life has been totally changed. Our village today has no one employed on the three farms that make up the parish and all the work is done by the farmers' own families or seasonal contractors. Today, you will hear no discussion of farming topics in the local pubs, the village allotments have reverted to pasture, no one makes cider and of course the farms do not smell like farms any more. Silage effluent poisons the stream from time to time and the grassland becomes more and more sour with the excessive amounts of slurry-manure pumped on it from the herds of dairy cows that are three or four times larger in numbers than our forebears would have deemed wise or profitable in the long run. In my own village, until some twenty years ago, we were never snowed-in in winter but now every snow-storm fills our access roads simply because the hedges that prevented drifting have all been grubbed out.

Many ideas were developed with the best of intentions after 1943, but the long term effects of some have proved disastrous. In order to improve the quality and milk-producing capacity of the national herd, official milk recording and artificial insemination were introduced. The result has been a glut of milk, stagnation of prices and consequent loss of profits to the farmers, as a result of the imposition of production quotas by the E.E.C. Initially, many were induced to increase the size of the herds to offset falling profits which, of course, only compounded the problem.

The research stations bred better grasses and clovers; the old pastures, with their hundreds of different herbs whose therapeutic effect is still largely not understood, were ploughed up to grow these new grasses. Today dairy cattle suffer milk-fever, 'staggers', and there are epidemics of many deficiency diseases that were either rare or simply unknown in my youth.

The universal call was for bigger and faster machines to do away with the maximum amount of manual labour. Hedges were removed to make room for them, resulting in soil erosion on an undreamed-of scale in East Anglia and the Fenlands. The few remaining hedges were massacred by machines that couldn't tell blackthorn from elder to the detriment of our wild bird-life.

I feel that most farm animals suffer a much poorer quality of life than ever with overcrowding both in buildings and outside in the fields. In the 1930s, I estimate we would call the vet on average less fields. In the 1930s, I estimate we would call the vet on average less than once a year to treat perhaps a case of summer mastitis or a difficult calving. More often than not, it was one of the old man's precious hunters that was poorly. On a large farm 3 miles from where I sit, they call their vet on average once a week throughout the year. Mastitis is a permanent condition leading to more antibiotics, fewer cures and the knacker's yard.

I have now passed my seventieth birthday and I look back on a life that I would not have changed for any other. Like most old folk I feel sad about a few things that have disappeared, leaving England a little poorer.

Some years ago Cogley Wood featured on the front page of *The Sunday Times*, in an article on the decline of our native woodlands. The writer said that until the wood was sold to an investor after the

The milk cart, 1930s. Dairy farmers often sold their produce direct to the customer. Before the use of bottles the milk was carried in churns and ladled out into the customer's own jugs.

the south-western peninsula of England of woodland that had been allowed to evolve without human interference, and contained a unique collection of flora and fauna. He was especially upset that the whole area had been bulldozed and planted with conifers. What had once been a glorious haven of every imaginable tree and shrub, where we picked blackberries and wild strawberries and watched for jays, pheasant, woodcock and nightingales and tried to trap foxes, stoats and weasels, was now a dark, dank, lifeless cemetery of a place. I went back once, but have no wish to repeat the trip.

Our old home, Horsley Farm, is still there, of course, though almost unrecognizable. Dutch Elm disease has killed off all the big trees that grew around each field; the two orchards have gone leaving the whole place looking bare and unfriendly; no one is employed by the owners and no cows, pigs or poultry are kept; there is just a collection of hunters and brood-mares.

My biggest regret is that none of the generations that follow ours will ever experience the pleasure of the old fields, hedges, ponds and woods and the wildlife that inhabited them – the daily companions of my youth that I loved so passionately.

CHAPTER TWELVE

A FARM WORKER IN CUMBRIA

Mr John Park of Underbarrow describes work on a small farm in Cumbria in the 1930s. He describes the hiring fairs which continued in that district for longer than they did in the south.

I was brought up on a farm and subsequently worked on several farms in this area. I was the second of eight children, five boys and three girls. The farm was the average size around here, about 70 acres, including some fruit trees. This area, the Lyth Valley, was and still is quite well known for white damson blossom. The farm could be worked by my father and one man or lad which meant that when we left school at fourteen we worked at home for a while before finding other work.

We lived a fair way from any town; Kendal was nearest, about 6 miles away. The only chance of a job was to go and work on other farms. The only work we knew anything about was farm work and it was more or less taken for granted that we would all end up farming ourselves, which my brothers all did eventually. My turn to go out to work came when I was seventeen. The work force on farms in those days comprised almost entirely single men and boys who were hired for a period of six months and lived on the farm.

A hiring fair was held in Kendal at Whitsuntide and Martinmas. If you wanted a job on a farm that is where you went and took your chance. My turn came at Martinmas in 1932. I have often heard this method of hiring described as degrading but in my opinion it was a very fair system. There was no fixed wages or hours in those days and you simply bartered with the farmer for the best wage you could get. You went to the hiring fair and stood in a particular street; farmers would come along, look you over, ask how much you wanted for six months and you tried to do a deal. Now I had a slight advantage in that I had been brought up on a farm, I could milk a cow by hand when I was ten, could plough with a pair of horses when I was fourteen, and by the time I was seventeen I could do any job on a mixed farm.

A lot of men and boys at those hiring fairs came from the towns in what was then the Furness district of Lancashire. This was a time of high unemployment and if you could get a job on a farm at least you had board and lodging for six months, if very little money.

The first farmer to ask me about a job was a man I knew slightly; after I had told him all about myself and how much I wanted for the six months, he rather floored me by saying I was too good for him, and that he was wanting someone a bit cheaper. I did, however, get hired eventually at a farm about 10 miles from Kendal and about the same distance from my own home, for the princely sum of £17 for six months.

Now up to the age of seventeen I had lived at home where I knew everybody and where there was some social life with village dances and whist drives and a working men's club. Now I found myself on an isolated farm, miles from anywhere where I knew no one at all. It was a rather shattering experience, but one shared by many in those days. You were hired for six months and you did not get paid until the end of the term, so you had to be fitted up with enough working clothes to last the six months and some pocket money. I took with me for that first six months two 10s (£1) notes and I had some of it left at the end of the time. The only time I went out was on a Saturday night when I biked 10 miles to Kendal and went to the 'pictures' (cinema).

This first farm I worked on was typical of farms in this area at the time. It was between 80 and 100 acres and reared stock with some sheep. You worked from 6 a.m. to 6 p.m. six days a week, with about three hours morning and night on Sundays milking the cows and feeding them and the other stock. At meal times you were only allowed enough time to eat your food and then it was back to work. Looking back one cannot help thinking it was a hard life but one must remember that farming methods had changed very little for hundreds of years.

The only power on farms was horsepower. Nobody in this area had a tractor until the Second World War. The only major changes up to then had been the horse-drawn mowing machine and the steam-driven threshing machine; previously all grass and corn was cut with a scythe and corn was threshed by hand with a flail. At that time most farms were practically self-supporting; besides cutting grass for hay most farmers would also have a few acres of oats and root crops. This provided enough feed for the stock in winter. Housekeeping was similar and I can remember my mother only had groceries delivered once a month at a time when she was feeding a family of ten. Included in the groceries every month was a 10 stone bag of flour which she mostly used to make into bread.

In about 1935 a milk factory was built at Milnthorpe, 8 miles south of Kendal. They began collecting milk all over this area so many farmers began to keep more dairy cattle. Another change which has taken place and which I find regrettable is the decrease in the number of agricultural holdings. In the parish of Underbarrow, where I live, there were about forty farms in 1940, now there are only about twenty.

Going to the blacksmiths. (Mr Park)

Waiting outside the smithy in Cumbria. (Mr Park)

139

Fitting a new iron tyre to a cart wheel. The iron hoop was heated until it expanded enough to be fitted over the wooden cart wheel. Cold water was then poured over it to make it contract and fit tightly on to the rim of the wheel. (Mr Park)

Cutting peat in Cumbria. (Mr Park)

Children pulling a hand-drawn seed drill in Cumbria. (Mr Park)

Sheep dipping in Cumbria. (Mr Park)

CHAPTER THIRTEEN

A LINCOLNSHIRE SMALLHOLDER AND FARM WORKER

Mr Albert Mason's father was a farm foreman who went on to rent a smallholding. It was difficult to make a living with this, so his father also helped on another farm. Albert worked on a farm after leaving school and became an active Trade Unionist.

I was born on 21 July 1915, at Car Farm, Winterton, that is about 7 miles from Scunthorpe. My dad was foreman at the farm and mother had my brother and myself as well as the wagoner and second chap to look after.

I cannot remember a lot about the first few years but I do remember starting school. We had 3 miles to walk; there were no buses in those days, and there was no canteen at the school, so we had to take our dinners with us. My brother, who was two years older than me went with me on the first day; usually some of the mothers went along but our mother had too much to do, so we had to go on our own. I never really liked school even from the beginning and I always looked forward to leaving at 4 p.m. in the afternoon, so I could return home where we used to play in the stackyard and wander round watching the men looking after their horses and the cattle. There wasn't the machinery in those days that there is today so it wasn't so dangerous.

I can remember the first day I was at school. I didn't seem to get on very well with the boys but eventually I got used to it. It was a mixed school and we had all kinds of games including hopscotch, rounders and all the usual things that children played in those days. As we got older we played football and cricket. The schoolmaster used to play for Winterton Professional Team and he was a really good cricketer; he used to put coins on the wickets and let us have a go, and if we were lucky enough to knock the bales off, we got the money. I remember as kids we used to get up to all sorts of tricks and the one thing I always liked doing was throwing stones. If I saw a bird or anything perched anywhere, I had a shot at it!

On the farm in those days there was no machinery, everything was done by horses. We also had cattle and sheep so quite a lot of men were employed. We always looked forward to weekends, Saturdays especially, when we used to play around the yard.

We had two schools in Winterton, the village being 5 miles from the steel town of Scunthorpe. They were the Church of England school and the Council School. We went to the Council School and in bad weather, especially when the snow was on the ground, we used to have a go at snowballing when one school met the other.

In the evenings during the summer and on Saturday mornings we used to help my father who was foreman on the farm. We helped to feed the calves and pigs and also to collect the eggs and do all the odd jobs. As soon as we were old enough, we had to chop the firewood for mother and do all the little jobs. There was always something to do. I got to like school better after the first year and I had some really nice friends. I always knew what I wanted to do when I left school. My father was a real good farm worker and after he became foreman, he could do practically everything there was to do on a farm in spite of being only 5 ft 1 in tall. I promised myself that was what I wanted to do when I left school.

The schools were quite antiquated compared to the way things are today. There was tap water but the toilets were just the awkward ones with wooden seats; a man used to come round every week and empty them. The lighting was gas lamps when I first started school, but when I was about twelve years old we had a new school with electric light. I was always good at arithmetic. I was untidy sometimes with my work making blots on my papers and I got the cane. I was never very good at history or geography. At election time, politics came into our lives. The Headmaster used to try and tell us what they meant and what they stood for. I can always remember that my father was Conservative and I think in those days you had to be what the farmer was. As I grew older I began to think quite differently. I remember the coal strike in 1926, it really was some strike. We had no coal and we needed it for the fires as there was no electricity in those days. We had to look for wood to burn. I can remember going down to the big thorn hedge in a grass field to get some wood. We used to chop down the trees and the boys used to trim them up and help the men to load them onto carts and bring them back home where we had to saw logs for firewood.

As I was growing up I used to watch my father when he was stacking the corn in harvest time and doing all the other jobs. He used to do a lot of draining because it was very heavy land and I used to remark how easily he seemed to do it. He was a very small man, but it was surprising what he could do and the strength he had especially at threshing time when there was 16 stones of corn to carry.

We really enjoyed being at the farm but eventually in March when I was twelve years old, the farmer decided to let the farm and go to Winterton where he had a little farm of his own. I remember the sale really well and we had the day off school; it was quite fun helping the men to round up the cattle and put them in the pens at the sale ring for selling. We used to run errands and take the sheets for the auctioneers into the house for the clerks to reckon them all up.

We left the farm on 6 April and Dad rented a smallholding, about a mile from where we had previously lived. It was only about 10 acres so my father had to go to work and we had to help him. I was about eleven then and we used to help him do odd jobs on the farm. Father bought one horse and we had two cows and one sow in pig. Dad borrowed horses from the farm where he worked to drill the land and work it all. We had a big garden and one day father asked me if I would like to plough it with our horse. I was chuffed – that was the start of what I wanted to do when I left school.

Farming was not very good in those days, however. I remember there was a Conservative government and it did not seem to put much money into farming. We had a litter of eight pigs which we took to Scunthorpe market; we came back with under £5, which even in those days wasn't very much for all the time and work that had been put in.

Eventually I remember leaving school at fourteen, it was on Friday 23 July. I ran home and said to Mother, 'I'll be ready for work tomorrow', but Dad said I should start on Monday, not bother with Saturday morning. It was harvest time and so I went to work on the farm where Dad worked and they were loading wheat. There were two brother farmers who owned the farm with just Dad and myself working. We went out with two wagons to load some wheat and when we got into the field, Dad was loading into one wagon with one brother and I had to load in the other with the other brother. It was the first time I had ever loaded sheaves and they were quite big, I was under 5 ft tall then and the sheaves were nearly as big as me. The farmer, being the boss, was very keen and he kept throwing the sheaves up. They were so big I couldn't spread many in the middle. Eventually the load got wider and wider and he said at the finish, 'The thundering thing won't go through the gate!' But it did. When we got to the stackyard, the stack was very nearly finished; it only wanted about three more loads. First off, father was stacking and one of the brothers emptied father's wagon and I was taking away on the stack. When it came to my wagon, they told me I had to unload it myself. Well, only being very small and the stack high up, I had to have a real long fork and it was really hard work putting those sheaves up there! This carried on all day and by the time we had finished at 7 p.m., I was glad to get home. I was so tired when I got home, I started to cry.

We had three weeks harvesting like that and I received 11s a week. It doesn't seem a lot of money for all the labour I put in. After the harvest, the brothers said they did not have any work for me and I had to leave. I went to work for another farmer nearby and I helped put in winter wheat. Then I helped with the cattle in the stockyard during the winter. We did weekly work on the farm in winter, mostly threshing and feeding the stock. In spring it was time for drilling barley and oats. I also had to work the horses and really enjoyed it. When it came round to hay time and harvest, it was quite a good job. After harvest the farmer said he could not keep me on because he hadn't enough money to keep me during the winter. I was thirteen weeks out of work, for five of which there was no dole and I just had my card stamped. The rest of the time I went round what we called 'tramp threshing'. I was following the threshing machine wherever it went to all the farms in our area and I really enjoyed that because I got paid the same money as the men, which was quite a lot more than 11s a week.

When May came round the following year, my father said he thought I ought to go to service, because he couldn't afford to keep me if I was out of work half the time. I went to a farm in Winterton where they kept two men, a wagoner and second lad. I had £15 a year and my food and lodgings with the foreman. After that year the foreman retired and they got a married wagoner and didn't bother with a second one. During those years we still went to chapel on a Sunday as we were brought up in the Christian faith.

After this I went to Limestone Farm, where I had six horses to look after and had to carry corn weighing 16 and 18 stones in a sack. It was jolly hard work. We were up at 5.30 a.m. to feed and

146

groom the horses ready for work at 6.30 a.m. We ploughed and worked until 2.30 when we went to the foreman's for dinner. The rest of the afternoon we looked after our horses. We got £1 a week and our food, for about 60 hours' work a week.

It was then I thought about joining the union. I was eighteen years of age. I could see that it was time we all got together and tried to make a better wage for the farm workers and improve our conditions. I carried on at the farm for two years and then I got married and remained there until the war broke out.

In April 1939 I went to Thornton Curtis as a married wagoner and my life changed quite a bit then. The farmer had one son who belonged to the Yeomanry before the war and when war broke out he had to go into the Regular Army. The farmer asked me if I would look after the farm because he lived some distance away and was very nearly sixty years of age. He said if I looked after everything well he would give me a 30 stone pig and I could have a dozen eggs every week extra. It was something I had been looking forward to for quite a while. I had to look after the cows when they were calving; we had quite a number of horses and we used to breed shire foals. In the wintertime I used to have as many as ten horses in the stables and in the yards to look after. We had just got a tractor. I did the corn drilling and a lot of the ploughing as it was very heavy land. Harvest time and threshing involved very heavy work; we used to employ prisoners of war. We got some very heavy crops of wheat and at threshing time I was the only one who could carry corn. Sometimes I used to carry as much as 50 or 60 quarters of corn, that is in 18 and 16 stone bags up into the granary. In those days there were no hoists or forklifts to help ease the labour.

I had been there just over a year when the secretary of the union passed away and the other members asked me if I would take over as Branch Secretary. I had always been keen on being in the union after first joining and so I said I would. I got to know quite a number of other people through going to meetings. As the war

147

progressed we all had to do something and I joined the Home Guard. We really enjoyed ourselves in those days but there wasn't much village life in war time and it was nice to get out, especially on Sundays and to meet other people and learn what was going on.

When the war finished, I left Thornton Curtis and went to manage a farm for a widow at South Ferriby, a bit nearer Winterton where my parents still lived. It was a 120 acre farm and was just what I had been looking for really. I had to give up the Secretary's job of the union and I got transferred into the Ferriby branch. My employer gave me a free hand at running the farm as she didn't know anything about working the land; she looked after the paperwork and did all the booking and ordering of things that we wanted. We had four horses at first. But as our land was on the Wold and the farmhouse was in the village we decided to buy one tractor. We sold two of our horses to do this and we just had the one tractor and two other horses to do the drilling. We farmed the old four-field system which I still thought was the best way of farming, although bigger farmers now were going out of cattle and sheep and going in for growing nothing but grain. We found the other was a much better way as I had to run the farm myself with one boy, whom I hired when he left school. We also had to make a living for the farmer's widow. We still kept the same system of sowing wheat then roots, followed by barley and then seeds again, and we ran the sheep on the seeds and put the manure from the foal yards on the seeds.

Farming then was just beginning to change and the first combines came into the village. I could see that eventually they would replace the binder. Ours was a small farm and we could not afford a combine, so we still kept on with our binder and did the drilling with a tractor and the horses. We ran as many cattle and sheep as we could on a small farm.

Village life was beginning to pick up after the war and things were getting back to normal. I could see the change coming, however, as farms were getting more equipment. They were not needing so many men. But we carried on the same way with one boy. Of course, he was getting older every year and he wanted more money. We really had a successful farm although it was small and it was very hard work but I thoroughly enjoyed it and I learnt a lot more than I had ever done before. I learned to clip sheep and look after them in lambing time. But in 1960 my employer told me that she was thinking of retiring the following year; she had to give a year's notice to the owner so it meant that we had to sell up in 1961.

The sale time came round and I was looking out for another job. Eventually I found something entirely different. It was on a small farm devoted simply to fruit and vegetables. It was at Barton on Humber, a matter of 5 miles from where I lived. I got the job and eventually started there in April 1961. It was a change from all I had been used to but I soon got interested in growing fruit. Mr Hargreaves, my boss, gave me some books on fruit farming and said, 'You're in charge!' We had a contract for blackcurrants with Beechams Foods, which was marvellous because they supplied the boxes and collected the fruit. All we had to do was employ pickers and to pack them. In the autumn there were blackberries and they were sold to freezer factories. We carried on for three years and I was really enjoying it but then the wholesale fruit business began to come to an end. People were getting their own freezers and they weren't buying wholesale. Eventually we decided to go in for 'pick your own fruit' and that put a bigger responsibility on myself and one woman I had working regularly for me in the farm shop. It was a job looking after people and keeping them from not spoiling the fruit especially when picking strawberries, as they wandered about looking for the best fruit. But it was fun; we were meeting people and coming into contact with all kinds from all walks of life, so it was quite interesting.

The village life in Barton was improving. The one thing I could see changing, however, was that the smaller shops were being forced out by the big supermarkets. I remember the first one opening in Barton; it really did change things altogether. The small people could not compete because the supermarkets could buy food wholesale and cheaper than the smaller men, and in turn could sell it cheaper. We were able to sell soft fruit during the season to the supermarkets. Eventually, we got our own freezer as we had so much fruit at times and never enough people to pick, so we decided to freeze our own. We also put some land down and started growing vegetables for people to come and pick.

By 1970, small villages seemed to be disappearing and some didn't even have a post office and possibly only one shop. People began to have motor cars and travelled to the supermarkets. It was difficult for the older people who had no other transport as buses were few and far between. Some of the village schools also closed down and all this change was really doing away with village life.

Our union still kept on although we were losing quite a number of members as people became unemployed. I had been at Barton about three years when the secretary left farm work and went to the steel works. I was Chairman so they asked me if I would take over as secretary as well, which I did. Farm workers were becoming redundant and empty farm cottages were being bought up by townspeople as weekend cottages.

On our farm, where there was a lot of manual work we eventually did the spraying and a number of other jobs by tractor. But there was still quite a bit of work to be done manually and I had to get women staff in for the weeding and fruit picking.

Barton was a fairly big town and had two football teams as well as two cricket teams. Social life wasn't too bad at all. Things were beginning to change and the biggest change was unemployment. There were only two major factories in Barton: the chemical works and the ropery, but they were cutting down on staff too and there wasn't the trade for ropes and fertilizers that there had been.

I have really had a wonderful and healthy life and would do it all over again if I had the chance. I would advise all young men, if they are interested in farming, and would like to make a career of it, to study agriculture and to join the union.

CHAPTER FOURTEEN

A WELSH FARMER'S DAUGHTER

Mrs Bradford of Rhuddlan in Clwyd was born on a small farm and she describes the hardships of life in the 1930s.

My father farmed a small mixed farm and supplemented his income by working on the roads, carting stone from the nearby quarry. My mother and the boys and girls helped with the hand milking and field work. Mother also sold buttermilk from the door as we were about 1½ miles from a village. I was second youngest in the family and we younger ones of her now large family walked to the village school, there and back. Sometimes the older boys had to stay away from school to help with the harvest. Once when the vicar called to see why my parents were not at church he found my father sowing wheat. He told my father what a wicked man he was. I was sure the corn would be a failure. But this was during the First World War when food was vital.

In the summer of 1924 my father bought a bigger farm of 400 acres and a much bigger house with twenty-two rooms in all counting attics, cellars and a large kitchen which had previously been used for cheese-making. My mother came from a Cheshire cheese-making family and my parents wanted to carry on along these lines. There were plenty of farm buildings of the old type:

low roofs, shippons with wooden stalls, and hay lofts above. All the wooden fittings in the shippons had to be scrubbed with disinfectant and whitewashed once a year. This usually happened in May when the cows were sleeping out at night. A hot sunny day was chosen for the work which was very hard. Great buckets of limewash were sloshed on all the doors. Ringworm on cattle was very prevalent in those days and this was one way of controlling it. One of my brothers would have to harness the cart-horse and walk 3 miles to the nearest lime quarry for the stuff; it took nearly all of one day.

At the end of the day washing ourselves entailed a continuous train of buckets of water from the rainwater butt at the back door, to a large boiler in the corner of one of the back kitchens, which also housed the bath. The ovens were also here, where the weekly bread was baked; they were heated by wood from the small wood and copse on the farm. Here was a job for the younger members of the family, gathering enough wood to get the oven white hot – and how we complained at that task. All the cooking was done on a range, a black-leaded side oven supplemented by a temperamental paraffin stove.

My mother fed all the cowmen, the extra Irish paddies for potato harvesting, the family and their friends of all ages, who came to the farm to help, play, or to go rabbiting or shooting, to play cards or do a bit of carting. She made gallons of ginger, nettle or dandelion wine for the harvest time, which in those days of turning and cocking the hay by pitchfork lasted from June until September. When the hay was finished and stacked then it was time for the corn harvest, yet another slow procedure.

Only the outside of the field was cut by scythe which had to be very sharp indeed. Today it is almost a lost art to hone the blades. I reckon my dad was an expert at it. Then the old horse binder came in after the canvas sails had been overhauled. At that time we only had two cart-horses, Prince and Lion. After the binders came the stooking, that is putting six to eight sheaves to lean against one

152

another and shaped like a pyramid to let the wind through to dry them and to keep the rain out. The art was to interlock sheaves so the wind didn't blow them down. Some of us were not very expert and then the strong winds would blow the stooks over. We had some hard words spoken to us and had to go and re-do them. If the weather was very bad this could go on for weeks and we could get very dispirited indeed.

There was great excitement for us when our turn came for the threshing machine. This great machine would come rumbling down the lane, at least a mile to the farm; it was painted red and belched out great black smoke. The driver was black from head to foot and I was very wary of him as I had never seen a black man even if he was only covered in coal dust. This was the only time I remember coal at the farm. We did from time to time have a cart load of coke from the gas works. It was exciting watching the men pitch the sheaves and the corn run down into the sacks, which then had to be carried up the twelve stone steps to the granaries. It was very hard on the knees and backs, and it was a very long day. All our stock feed for the winter and our bread for the year depended on this day. All our wheat was taken to the local miller.

After the corn harvest it was straight into winter ploughing; there didn't seem to be much time for holidays or much pleasure.

Between 1924 and 1939 my father increased his stock. He reared shorthorn cows which were dual purpose, giving milk and beef on the bone when sold. My brothers helped my father to build up a good dairy business with two carts doing a retail milk round. They were very smartly turned out. The churns had brass bands around them that had to be cleaned every day, the harness was polished with saddle soap, and the cart was kept clean. This was quite labour-intensive but in those days people had real pride in their turnout. My brothers had to wear stiff white coats and black shiny leggings, no sloppy jeans like today.

You may be aware of the terrible slump that came in the 1930s. My sister hauled baskets of eggs to the local market and could not

Feeding her pigs, from a postcard of about 1910. Most farm workers kept a few pigs and poultry to supplement their wages.

You may be aware of the terrible slump that came in the 1930s. My sister hauled baskets of eggs to the local market and could not get even 1*s* (5p) for thirty and would have to fetch them home again. It was a very distressing time for the farmers and many small farms went bankrupt. Father sold the farm and the boys went to work in the cities, all except my youngest brother who carried on

CHAPTER FIFTEEN

FARM WORK IN COUNTY DURHAM

Mr S. Glancey told me the following story of his life in County Durham during the 1930s. He was born in 1920 in Washington village. He told me his father had been an NCO in the Army and had trained to do the work of a blacksmith, saddler and horse-breaker-cum-vet. After his discharge from the Army in 1919 he became employed as a horsekeeper in charge of forty ponies at one of the local collieries. He describes the typical work carried out throughout the year on local farms.

At the age of ten, I became interested in my father's work at the six farms surrounding our village. He was in great demand for his knowledge of farming and horses. I was his disciple following him around and helping him in my own small way. Eventually I was accepted by the local farmers and their workers; all my summer evenings and holidays were spent on different farms until the Second World War started. I immediately volunteered for the RAF where I remained until 1946.

The six farms around the village were mixed dairy and crops; three were owned by gentlemen farmers with two or three hinds (labourers) working for them and three were working farmers with one or two hinds. They all had local part-time helpers for harvest and organic muck-spreadings. There were also four collieries in this area.

The hinds were housed in tied cottages near the farm and were on call twenty-four hours a day with Saturday afternoons off. They had a low wage plus a few 'fiddles' to boost their wages. Ailments like colds, flu, sprains and rheumatism were largely ignored and worked-off. Their skills at farming and machinery were very high. Most farmers never seemed to appreciate them, they were irritable and always had another job ready before the men had finished the task in hand. I helped the hinds a lot by harnessing horses, chopping turnips for the cows, milking, taking horses to the blacksmith for shoeing, feeding chickens, cleaning out stables and polishing the harness. By around 9 p.m. on a summer's night everyone was tired and exhausted. The hinds were glad to get home for a well-earned rest.

In winter the work to be done included the indoor feeding of the animals and cleaning them out. There were ditches to clear, fences to put up and repairs to be made in others, stables to whitewash, and vegetables to cart to market. There were fallow fields to lay out and plough for the frost to break up the soil for sowing in the spring. Farm buildings had to be repaired inside and out and a general clean out was done.

In spring the work was mainly ploughing, sowing, fertilizing and harrowing. Everything was always urgent. It was still a bit cold and often we were soaked to the skin – we would use potato sacks tied round our shoulders or as hoods against the chilly winds, boots were heavily coated with mud, aching arms tried to keep horses straight and jerk heavy ploughs around to complete furrows. Harrowing was a little easier; the harrow was a spiked contraption used to break up the soil, pulled by one horse with a hind walking behind the harrow. This was very tiring on the legs.

The crops that were grown were usually corn, wheat, oil, rape, turnips, potatoes, kale and clover. The mechanical device for sowing was the drill. The hind had a metal seat made comfortable with folded sacks to soften the ride. There was one horse in the shafts and the driver had various levers to regulate the depth and flow of the seeds from the loaded seed-box behind his seat. The seeds flowed down the hollow tines into the light furrow made by the curved tine and covered by the splay at the rear. The driver kept a watchful eye on the quantity of the seeds in the box. The following day, if fine, the field was rolled with a light roller, with one horse in the shafts.

Fertilizing was carried out by horse and cart with a part-time labourer spreading the organic matter. He stood in the loaded cart and forked the fertilizer onto the land.

Summer was the time for dawn to dusk operations. Before starting the harvest the corn had to be tested for ripeness by the farmer who rubbed some ears of corn between his hands and blew off the chaff to see, feel and smell what was left in his hands. There were anxious consultations about weather forecasts; if they were favourable, reaping started with one horse in trace chains and soon the reaper blades were taking their first cuts like miniature windmills and with the hinds seated on the binder body off they went. Then the first tied-up stooks rolled out of the side of the machine and were pounced upon by the part-timers and stacked in double rows ready for carting off to the thresher. The same procedures, with some variations, were applied to the other crops. The hay was piled into 6 ft high ricks and winched by hand onto flat tip-up horse-drawn 'bogeys', then winched level and carted off to the barns for winter feed. There the ricks were pitch-forked onto various levels of wooden platforms, dried out and baled and then made into a massive stack tied down with hay ropes and covered by large tarpaulin sheets which were pulled over the top and pegged down, thus securing them against wind and rain. It was a very skilled job to make a big stack. The layout had to allow for air passages which were vital to prevent overheating. During these summer operations the 'gaffers' were very demanding and tempers were short. The normal routine for the farm animals, of milking, feeding and mucking out was still part of the day with added pressure of harvesting. Threshing was the same but with the noise feeding and mucking out was still part of the day with added pressure of harvesting. Threshing was the same but with the noise of the steam engine and its flapping belts driving the thresher. Then the gaping jaws were fed with the corn stooks, ever moving and collecting on one side the baled-up straw and then stacking. On the other side the machine filled sacks of corn. The noise was deafening, the dust was everywhere and filtered through our scarves and handkerchiefs, and mouths were soon coated inside and eyes, ears and nostrils filled. This operation might last two days and the steam-engine driver was always keen to move on to the next lucrative job. It was a bit different from the picture-postcard idyll.

The farm workers had to be as strong as their Belgian horses and as untiring with their various loads. I don't remember any celebrations at the end of harvest as portrayed on the films. During

A fine pair of horses ready for work, 1930. (Mr Cooling)

of harvest time. He made sure he was paid by the absent-minded farmers and came away with a few perks for the household larder.

The main tasks in autumn were the harvesting of root crops and hedging. The potatoes were uncovered by a horse-drawn machine which scooped the plants to one side, then a large gang of women (provided by a South Shields private company who transported them to the field) began scooping the potatoes into baskets; once full they were weighed and credited to them, then bagged and put onto a lorry. These women were transported on flat lorries whatever the weather and started work at 8 a.m. It was back-breaking work; the hedges were their 'loos', snacks were short and most of these workers were middle-aged with skin like leather. They wore big shawls, long skirts and men's boots. Sunset brought an end to their labours, the lorries were loaded with sacks of potatoes and the women climbed on board and off they went, singing their songs such as 'We are the tatie pickers'. This was a signal for the local people to descend on the field with buckets and rakes to sort out potatoes the women had missed; these raids were very fruitful.

The harvesting of kale, turnips and swedes was a laborious task of lifting and hacking and throwing into carts. It was especially difficult after a wet spell, but it had to be done for winter feed and for the market. One of my tasks was preparing a mound of turnips for the cattle and pigs. I used a big mincing machine to chop the turnips ready for filling the troughs; it was laborious and dirty. It also enabled the hind to get on with other jobs.

Hedging and layering was a very skilled job for the hinds. Injuries were plenty and nasty scratches festered and often needed medical attention. There was stubble to fire, a stinking job that required a keen look-out for any wind changes. The next job of the year was to clean and grease the machines before storing them at the onset of winter.

These were just some of the tasks these splendid men performed in the farming year. These episodes remain fresh in my mind. The farm workers were a cheerful lot while they had their health and strength. In later years the weather and non-stop heavy tasks took their toll and these men soon showed their age. They would be racked with rheumatism and arthritis, chest infections and foot troubles. Eventually each job took that little bit longer, and there were younger men seeking employment and the spectre of notice to quit the tied cottage became a real threat.

The farm machines I see used today are simply fantastic; gone is the toil out of farming. The tractors with their all-weather cabins, comfortable seats, radio playing, warm atmosphere inside, must be a joy to drive. The speed with which they can plough and harrow a field is really something to see. There are numerous special machines on the market, some of which can be adjusted to other purposes and it isn't any wonder our farmers are so efficient. The hinds must be good mechanics now, on top of their other skills. Farming has made great strides with the use of silos, battery hen-coops, chicken incubators, Dutch barns, balanced diets, selective stock breeding, polystyrene sheets and bags, and artificial insemination of cattle. My only doubts concern the use of all the chemicals on crops and soils; they increase the yield per acre but the effects on the soil and wildlife may upset the balance of nature. I notice now a number of farms advertising, 'All produce organically grown'. They are finding good markets. People are starting to complain about the mysterious aches and pains in their stomachs and the tasteless vegetables. Our greengrocer who has a big mobile round, complains bitterly about the skin rashes he has brought about by handling produce from the markets. Chemical research in various countries is very haphazard; some ban certain chemicals, fertilizers and pesticides, while other countries use them freely despite evidence of toxins. More research and rulings must be made, otherwise public health will suffer together with that of the livestock that drink the polluted waters draining from the fields.

I, therefore, give my vote to the 1930s for wholesome food. Modern-day farming gives good yields and speed but has great problems to solve.

APPENDIX

FARMERS AND WRITERS

In seeking information on farming and country life in the first half of the twentieth century we naturally turn to published works. Many books on those subjects have been published but few of them have been written by working farmers or farm workers. The average farmer is too busy and in any case is more interested in getting on with the practical work than in writing about it. There have been some exceptions to this general rule and we may gain much information from their publications.

The best known of these authors was A.G. Street. Arthur Street, known to everyone as A.G., was born in 1892. He was the son of a farmer and after leaving Dauntsey's School at West Lavington near Devizes he worked on his father's farm until he reached the age of nineteen. He then emigrated to Canada where he worked on a farm in Manitoba until 1914. He returned to Britain and volunteered for the Army at the start of the First World War. He was rejected and returned to work on his father's farm until 1917 when his father died. A.G. then took over the tenancy of Ditchampton Farm where he farmed until 1951. When the Ditchampton area became covered with new housing estates he decided to move and was offered the tenancy of Mill Farm on the other side of the Wylye Valley which was on the estates of the Earl of Pembroke. There he lived until his death in 1966.

A.G. had married in 1918 and like most farmers he enjoyed the prosperity of the immediate post-war period. This was short-lived and during the farming depression of the 1920s he had a hard struggle to avoid bankruptcy. In 1929 he caught influenza and in his enforced idleness was so incensed by an article on farming in the *Daily Mail* that he wrote a reply. It was published in the newspaper and he received three guineas for his efforts. This success led him to write other articles and he became a regular contributor to the *Farmer's Weekly* for thirty years. Edith Oliver, a popular novelist of the time, encouraged him to write a novel. So it was in this way that *Farmer's Glory* came to be published in 1932. It was based on his own experiences and is one of the finest books on farming and country life of that period. It received rave reviews and his work was compared to that of Cobbett. The book became required reading in many schools as part of the English curriculum for the School Certificate.

A.G.'s second novel *Strawberry Roan* followed the next year. In this the story centres around the life of a calf called Strawberry Roan which is moved from farm to farm, and in the course of telling its tale Street draws a picture of rural life full of incident and spiced with humour. In all he published thirty-four books which included not only novels but also factual works on farming and country life. He also became a well-known broadcaster.

A near contemporary of Street's, Adrian Bell, born in 1901, became a farm pupil in Suffolk after leaving school at Uppingham. His experiences on a farm at Benfield are beautifully described in *Corduroy,* published in 1930. At the end of the book he described how he took over his own first small farm.

He continued his story in subsequent books, *Silver Ley* and *The Cherry Tree*. In a later work called *Sunrise to Sunset* (1944) he describes life in wartime on a farm in Westmorland where he had sent his wife and children while he continued to work on his own farm in Suffolk.

Henry Williamson presents a very different case from Street and Bell, for he was an author who became a farmer. When he took up

162

farming he was already famous as the author of *Tarka the Otter* (1927) and *Salar the Salmon* (1935). These books describe the lives of these two creatures and both are the result of careful observation coupled with an ability to imagine the inner experiences of these animals.

Williamson was born in 1895 and brought up in rural Bedfordshire. As a boy he was much influenced by the work of Richard Jefferies, the writer on wildlife and the countryside whose book *Hodge and his Masters*, published in the 1880s, paints a vivid picture of rural life in the 1870s.

After serving in the Army during the First World War, Williamson attempted to take up a career as a journalist in London. Urban life, however, did not suit him and he left to live in a cottage on Exmoor where he wrote a series of novels called *The Flax of Dream* which were centred round the life of the cousin of Phillip Maddison, hero of *A Chronicle of Ancient Sunlight*. The first of these, *The Beautiful Years*, appeared in 1921 and it was followed by *Dandelion Days* (1922), *The Dream of Fair Women* (1924) and *The Pathway* (1928). By the mid-1930s he had published several other works but his novels were not specifically on farming or country life. In 1936, in spite of the fact that he had no experience of farming, he decided to buy a farm in Norfolk. In 1941 he published *The Story of a Norfolk Farm* in which he described the problems he encountered in running a farm during a period in which agriculture was still suffering from the effects of the Depression. It has been described as his best book and gives a wonderfully clear account of farming at that time.

One of the best series of books on farming and country life by a farmer is that by Fred Archer. In these books Archer sets out to present a picture of changes in country life in the village of Ashton under Hill in the county of Worcestershire between 1876 and 1939. He describes in vivid detail the daily lives of the inhabitants of that village. He published an autobiography *Fred Archer – Farmer's Son* which describes his memories of childhood in the 1920s and also *The Village Doctor* which gives an account of the role of the doctor in country life through the biography of Edward Roberson who was the doctor in Ashton for forty years.

Another farmer turned writer was Ralph Whitlow who is perhaps most widely remembered for his broadcasts and the articles that appeared in a wide range of journals including the *Daily Telegraph* and *The Times*. He was Farming Editor of *The Field* and had a regular column in *The Guardian Weekly*. He published over a hundred books including two which are of particular interest – *A Family and a Village* (1968) and *The Lost Village*, appropriately subtitled 'Rural Life Between the Wars'.

One of the best-known writers and broadcasters on farming in the 1940s and '50s was Ralph Wightman. He had been brought up on a farm and became a lecturer on Agriculture and Senior Agricultural Advisor to Dorset County Council. His book *Days on the Farm*, though written for young people, gives a fine account of farming methods on the farm in Dorset where he had been brought up and which was farmed by his elder brother who took over from his father in 1938.

There are also some very useful and interesting books written by ordinary farmers. One such book is *The Farming Ladder*, written by G. Henderson and first published in 1944. It ran into thirteen impressions by 1948. The author described his book as 'the plain unvarnished story of a farm and the people who have worked it over a period of twenty years. In it will be found none of the fine writing or sentimentality about farming which is the prerogative of other writers. If it helps others to make a success of their farming it will be well justified.'

In spite of the author's modesty it is a well-written account of the methods he used with considerable success on a small farm during a period when agriculture had been suffering a depression for some ten years.

A more recent publication is *On the Smell of an Oily Rag* by John Cherrington which was published in 1979. In this book he describes fifty years of farming mainly in England, though he spent some time in New Zealand and Argentina.

Inland Farm by R.M. Lockley has a strange title, for the farm in question is situated on the small island of Skokholm in the Bristol Channel. It gives fine descriptions of farming methods that differed little from those on the mainland. While a variety of crops was grown including wheat, rye, barley, oats and potatoes, the main crop was flax.

Other books produced by farmers include the writings of Justin and Edith Brooks who farmed in West Suffolk from 1927. Their book *Suffolk Prospect* provides an account of life in that county.

Wilfred Scott's book *To a Farmer Born* tells the story of life on 'an old Devon farm before the tractor'.

In 1922 George Sturt published *A Farmer's Life* which is the biography of his uncle. It contains much information on farming methods as well as the country life of that time.

There have also been a few farm workers who have picked up the pen to record their experiences of farming and country life during that period. One of the best of such books was *The Rabbit Skin Cap*, an autobiograpical account of life in Norfolk by George Baldry, which was published in 1939. A year later Fred Kitchen published *Brother to the Ox*, the story of his happy childhood in rural Yorkshire. Also from Yorkshire is *Pie for Breakfast* (1984) by Harry Reffolds who tells the story of his life as a farm worker from 1914 to the early 1920s.

John Stewart Collis wrote *The Worm Forgives the Plough* from a different perspective. He was a writer who took up a job as a farm worker during the Second World War.

On the whole, however, books on farming written by farmers and farm workers are few and far between. This is one of the reasons I have spent much time on the reminiscences recorded in this book and in the three previous works I have published. It would be a tragedy if these unique experiences were lost forever.

FURTHER READING

A number of books have been mentioned in the text and further details of these are given here, in addition to other books which are devoted to farming and country life that may be of interest to the reader. Places of publication are given only if outside London.

Anon. *In Pitstone Green there is a Farm*, Pitstone Local History Society, 1979.

Appleyard, J. *The Farm Tractor*, David & Charles, Newton Abbot, 1967.

Archer, Fred. *The Distant Scene*, Hodder & Stoughton, 1967.

——. *Under the Parish Lantern*, Hodder & Stoughton, 1969.

——. *The Secrets of Bredon Hill*, Hodder & Stoughton, 1971.

——. *A Lad of Evesham Vale*, Hodder & Stoughton, 1972. Reprinted by Alan Sutton Publishing, Stroud, 1991.

——. *Muddy Boots and Sunday Suits*, Hodder & Stoughton, 1973. Reprinted by Alan Sutton Publishing, Stroud, 1992.

——. *Golden Shraves and Black Horses*, Hodder & Stoughton, 1974.

——. *When Village Bells were Silent*, Hodder & Stoughton, 1975. Reprinted by Alan Sutton Publishing, Gloucester, 1988.

——. *Farmer's Son*, Whillet, 1984.

——. *A Country Twelvemonth*, Alan Sutton Publishing, Stroud, 1992.

Bain, Joan. *The Two Farms*, Robert Hale, 1989.

Baldry, George. *The Rabbit Skin Cap*, Collins, 1939.

Baldwin, N. *Farm Tractors*, Frederick Warne, 1977.

Beaven, Stanley. *Damsons By The Pound*, Brewin Books, 1993.

Bell, Adrian. *Corduroy*, Penguin, Harmondsworth, 1940.

——. *Sunrise to Sunset*, Lane, 1944.

——. *The Budding Morrow*, Lane, 1946.

Bell, Brian. *Fifty Years of Farm Machinery*, The Farming Press, Ipswich, 1993.

FURTHER READING

Blandford, Peter. *Old Farm Tools and Machinery*, David & Charles, Newton Abbot, 1976.

Bonnett, Harold. *Farming With Steam*, Shire Publications, Aylesbury, 1979.

Brigden, Roy. *Ploughs and Ploughing*, Shire Publications, Aylesbury, 1984.

Broom, Arthur. *Bob's Boy*, W. Poole, Norwich, 1984.

Buchan, James, *Thatched Village*, Hodder & Stoughton, 1983.

Collis, J.S. *The Worm Forgives the Plough*, Knight, 1973.

Culpin, Claude. *Farm Machinery*, Collins, 1986.

Davies, Peter. *Mare's Milk and Wild Honey*, André Deutsch Ltd, 1987.

Day, J. Wentworth. *Harvest Adventure*, Harrap, 1946.

Edwards, George. *From Crow-scaring to Westminster*, Labour Publishing, 1922.

Evans, George Ewart. *The Horse in the Furrow*, Faber, 1960.

——. *Ask the Fellows who Cut the Hay*, Faber, 1962.

——. *The Pattern under the Plough*, Faber, 1966.

——. *Where Beards Wag All*, Faber, 1970.

Groves, R. *Sharpen the Sickle*, Merlin Press, 1981.

Harrison, S. *Yorkshire Farming Memories*, Castle Museum, York, 1981.

Hauxwell, Hannah. *Hannah – The Complete Story*, Arrow Books, 1991.

Henderson, G. *The Farming Ladder*, Faber, 1944.

Hillyer, Richard. *Country Boy*, Hodder & Stoughton, 1967.

Home, Michael. *Autumn Fields*, Methuen, 1944.

How, R.W. *Good Country Days*, Hollis and Carter, 1946.

James, A. *Memories of a Fen Tiger*, David & Charles, Newton Abbot, 1986.

Ketteridge, Christopher and Mays, Spike. *Five Miles from Bunkum*, Eyre Methuen, 1972.

Kitchen, Fred. *Brother to The Ox*, Dent, 1940.

Lawson, Douglas. *Hand to the Plough*, Ashgrove Press, Sevenoaks, 1982.

Lockley, R.H. *Inland Farm*, Witherby, 1943.

Longhurst, S. and others. *Sherbourne A Cotswold Village*, Alan Sutton Publishing, Stroud, 1992.

Megginson, Irene *Mud On My Doorstep*, Hutton Press, Beverley, 1987.

Middleton, C.H. *Village Memories*, Cassell, 1941.

Moore, John. *A Portrait of Elmbury*, Collins, 1945.

Morgan, L. *A Plough On the Mountain*, Odhams, London, 1955.

Newby, H. *The Deferential Worker*, Lane, 1977.

Nial, Ian. *To Speed the Plough*, Heinemann, 1977.

Partridge, M. *Early Agricultural Machinery*, Evelyn, 1968.

Refford, Harry. *Pie for Breakfast*, Hutton Press, Beverley, 1984.

Rose, Walter, and Hockham, John. *Good Neighbours*, Cambridge University Press, Cambridge, 1942.

Scott, Wilfred. *To a Farmer Born*, Bristol Broadsides, Bristol, 1984.

Scott-Watson, J.A. *The Farming Year*, Longman Green.

Seymore, J. *Rural Life*, Select Editions, Devizes, 1993.

Smith, D.J. *Horse-drawn Farm Machines*, Shire Publications, Aylesbury, 1984.

Stewart, Sheila. *Lifting the Latch*, Oxford University Press, Oxford, 1986.

Street, A.G. *Farmer's Glory*, Faber, 1932.

——. *Strawberry Roan*, Faber, 1932.

——. *Country Calendar*, Eyre & Spottiswoode, 1935.

——. *Round the Year on the Farm*, Oxford University Press, Oxford, 1942.

Street, Pamela. *My Father – A.G. Street*, Hale, 1984.

Thompson, D. (ed). *Change and Tradition in Rural England*, Cambridge University Press, Cambridge, 1980.

Thompson, John. *Horse Drawn Farm Vehicles*, J. Thompson, Fleet, 1980.

Tylden, G. *Harness and Saddlery*, Shire Publications, Aylesbury, 1971.

Vince, J. *Carts and Wagons*, Shire Publications, Aylesbury, 1987.

Whitlow, Ralph. *A Family and a Village*, Baker, 1968.

——. *The Lost Village*, Hale, 1988.

Wightman, R. *Days on the Farm*, Hutchinson, 1952.

Williams, James. *Give Me Yesterday*, Country Book Club, 1973.

Williams, M. *Great Tractors*, Blandford, Poole, 1982.

Wilkes, Peter. *Illustrated History of Farming*, Spurbook, 1978.

Williamson, Henry. *The Story of a Norfolk Farm*, Faber, 1941.

Wormell, D. *Anatomy of Agriculture*, Harrap, 1978.